# PHYSIOLOGY

## OF

# INSECT DEVELOPMENT

# The Developmental Biology Conference Series, 1956

HELD UNDER THE AUSPICES OF

## THE NATIONAL ACADEMY OF SCIENCES
### NATIONAL RESEARCH COUNCIL

*Paul Weiss*

ORGANIZER AND GENERAL CHAIRMAN

---

THE CONFERENCES

## EMBRYONIC NUTRITION
*Brown University, July 23–24*
Chairman: J. S. NICHOLAS; *Reporter and editor:* DOROTHEA RUDNICK

## REGENERATION IN VERTEBRATES
*Brown University, July 23–24*
Chairman: E. G. BUTLER; *Reporter and editor:* CHARLES S. THORNTON

## CYTODIFFERENTIATION
*Brown University, July 27–31*
Chairmen: ERNST HADORN, HOLGER HYDÉN, W. E. ANKEL, V. B. WIGGLESWORTH, and ISAAC BERENBLUM; *Reporter and editor:* DOROTHEA RUDNICK

## ENVIRONMENTAL INFLUENCES ON PRENATAL DEVELOPMENT
*Jackson Memorial Laboratory, August 2–4*
Chairman: MEREDITH N. RUNNER; *Reporter and editor:* BEATRICE MINTZ

## IMMUNOLOGY AND DEVELOPMENT
*Jackson Memorial Laboratory, August 7–9*
Chairman: JAMES D. EBERT; *Reporter and editor:* MAC V. EDDS, JR.

## PHYSIOLOGY OF INSECT DEVELOPMENT
*Macdonald College, August 14–16*
Chairman: MAX F. DAY; *Reporter and editor:* FRANK L. CAMPBELL

## DYNAMICS OF PROLIFERATING TISSUES
*Brookhaven National Laboratory, September 5–8*
Chairman: C. P. LEBLOND; *Reporter and editor:* DOROTHY PRICE

## ENDOCRINES IN DEVELOPMENT
*Shelter Island, N.Y., September 11–13*
Chairman: B. H. WILLIER; *Reporter and editor:* RAY L. WATTERSON

## MITOGENESIS
*Argonne National Laboratory, September 24–26*
Chairman: AUSTIN M. BRUES; *Reporters and editors:* H. S. DUCOFF and C. F. EHRET

## WOUND HEALING AND TISSUE REPAIR
*Rockefeller Institute, October 2–4*
Chairman: FRANCIS D. MOORE; *Reporter and editor:* W. BRADFORD PATTERSON

# PHYSIOLOGY OF
# INSECT
# DEVELOPMENT

*v.6.*

*Edited by*

FRANK L. CAMPBELL

THE UNIVERSITY OF CHICAGO PRESS

*The Library of Congress Catalog Card*

⌐                                                          ¬

CONFERENCE ON PHYSIOLOGY OF INSECT DEVEL-
OPMENT, *Macdonald College, 1956.*

  Physiology of insect development, edited by
Frank L. Campbell. [Chicago] University of Chicago Press [1959].

   xiv, 167 p. illus., diagrs., tables. 24 cm. (The Developmental biology conference series, 1956)

   Condensed version of the proceedings of the conference.
   Bibliography: p. 166–167.

   1. Entomology—Congresses. 2. Insects—Development.
3. Embryology—Insects.   I. Campbell, Frank Leslie,
1898–   ed. II. Title.   (Series)

QL461.C54  1956          595.7            59–9701

Library of Congress

∟                                                          ⌟


THE UNIVERSITY OF CHICAGO PRESS, CHICAGO 37
Cambridge University Press, London, N.W. 1, England
The University of Toronto Press, Toronto 5, Canada

© 1959 by The University of Chicago. Published 1959
Composed and printed by THE UNIVERSITY OF CHICAGO PRESS
Chicago, Illinois, U.S.A.

# Preface to the Series

Development and growth have usually been studied rather piecemeal: as embryology, or plant physiology, or nutrition, or oncology; as seriation of stages of chick embryos, as cell division in fish eggs or plant root tips, as growth curves of children, as hormone response of plumage, as spread of a fungus, as repair of a broken bone or the swelling of a diseased spleen; by observation, measurement, comparison, chemical alteration, excision, transplantation, or sheer speculation. Yet, in reality, all these are merely isolated aspects of one broad continuous spectrum of phenomena, varied manifestations of the same basic principles and elementary processes—multiplication of organic mass (growth); diversification of that mass (differentiation); pattern formation (morphogenesis); progressive change (maturation and aging); and the repair or reproduction of patterns after disturbance (regulation and regeneration).

This unity of subject matter has received renewed emphasis in the "Developmental Biology Conference Series of 1956," a record of which is now presented in ten volumes, including the present report. The series consisted of co-ordinated and interdisciplinary conferences, symposia, and workshops, organized under the sponsorship of the Biology Council of the Division of Biology and Agriculture, National Academy of Sciences–National Research Council, with the generous financial support of governmental agencies, industrial organizations, and private foundations and donors (see list at end of Preface).

The Conference Series brought together experts from the fields of anatomy, biochemistry, biometry, biophysics, botany, cytology, embryology, endocrinology, genetics, histology, immunology, microbiology, neurology, nutrition, oncology, pathology, physiology, radiology, and zoölogy, from the United States and abroad, less for a display of most recent technical advances than for a concerted examination and evaluation of the contributions of these various specialties to the elucidation of focal issues of developmental biology. Fresh orientation and new ideas could be expected to emerge from this pool of critically distilled knowledge by the intersection of formerly unrelated trends of thought or by the discovery of common cores in formerly unrelated sets of data. Nearly three hundred American and fifty-four foreign scientists (from nineteen countries) joined in this task.

To serve the outlined objective, the meetings had to be ruled by the key words: *perspective* and *relevance*. All participants were admonished to present only such itemized information, conclusions, demonstrations, criticisms, illustrations, questions, and quotations as promised to throw light on the *issue* under discussion; that is, to confine themselves to comments of "strategic" or "catalytic" pertinence, not merely adding to the bulk of information, but contributing to clarification, order, harmonization, and comprehensibility. Pertinent comments, however, were welcomed regardless of whether they referred to data so new as to be still largely unknown; so old as to have been widely forgotten; so specialized or technical as to have received limited currency among "outsiders"; so theoretical as to have escaped the practitioners; or so "self-evident" as to have evaded critical scrutiny. Each participant was expected to draw from his store of special knowledge points that might help correct misinterpretations, indicate the feasibility of new approaches, and, above all, reveal existing gaps of knowledge and understanding.

It is evident that a group exercise of this complexion, with free give-and-take, could not possibly "cover the ground" in any of the selected topics within the given time limits and without sacrificing spontaneity, informality, and depth of penetration. Often a few key issues, profoundly analyzed and critically elucidated, proved far more enlightening than a hurried bird's-eye view of a large field. In cases in which workers from different disciplines were only vaguely acquainted with one another's stock-in-trade and vocabulary, the time and effort spent on describing even elementary facts in order to provide a common ground for communication proved very worthwhile, indeed. In other instances, where the facts were familiar but their interpretation was controversial, it seemed preferable to let argumentation take precedence over the recital of facts.

The foregoing remarks are intended to explain the discursive nature of these volumes. In conferences which combine basic and clinical interests, technical and theoretical approaches, molecular and organismic concepts, botanical and zoölogical subjects, biochemical and morphological aspects, it is imperative to place the reconciliation and synthesis of viewpoints above all other considerations.

In line with this general precept, each conference chairman was to open his meeting with a brief keynote address, staking out the major problems for discussion. By phrasing questions, rather than stating theses, he was to set the stage for free, though not necessarily unpremeditated, participation. Most of the conferences were closed meetings, with attendance confined to the invited panel members. In a few cases, auditors were admitted. Only the symposia at Brown University, which were co-sponsored by the International Union of Biological Sciences, were open to the general public.

For the purpose of publication, an experienced scientist familiar with the subject matter was appointed as official reporter and editor for each conference, to attend all sessions without taking part in the discussions. From the sound-tape recordings of the proceedings and his or her own notes, each editor then produced a condensed version of the conference. These accounts constitute the substance of this series of publications.

The individual reports vary greatly in form, depending on the topic and organization of each conference as well as on the personal predilections of the editor. Only in one instance has the dialogue style been kept, and, even so, only after considerable pruning. In other cases, an entire conference has been reported as a third-person account, reordering the text rather liberally into a logical sequence by combining related fragments; in this process of synthesis, an editor assumed the full prerogatives of an author. Most of the reports, however, range somewhere between these two extremes, abstracting the major comments of the various participants without obliterating their identity, yet resorting to verbal quotations infrequently or not at all. Some participants furnished their own rewritten versions of the factual presentations, and these were in most cases inserted in the text as such. In all cases, the participants were given an opportunity to check their respective contributions, either in the original transcript or later in the condensed and revised text.

The lack of uniformity reflects the informal spirit of the meetings and accents the main theme of the Conference Series: that developmental biology is currently in a state of flux, fitting no rigid mold and shaping its own course as it gains momentum by the growth and confluence of its many tributaries. It is hoped that the publication of this series will add to that momentum, as did the conferences themselves.

To each of the participants and, above all, to the chairmen and editors, we owe a deep debt of gratitude. To the following donors of funds, we reiterate our appreciation for generous assistance: Atomic Energy Commission, U.S. Departments of the Air Force, Army, and Navy (Medical Services); Office of Naval Research; Fulbright Fellowship Program; National Institutes of Health; National Science Foundation; International Union of Biological Sciences; American Cyanamid Company; Diamond Alkali Company; Merck and Company, Inc.; Chas. Pfizer and Company, Inc.; Rohm and Haas Company; E. R. Squibb and Sons; American Cancer Society; and Rockefeller Foundation. Special thanks are due to Dr.

Russell B. Stevens, executive secretary of the Biology Council, for carrying the major load in the recording of the conferences; and to Mrs. Geraldine A. Norton, administrative assistant, for her effective help with the preparations and practical details of the meetings.

PAUL WEISS

NEW YORK CITY
May 1958

CONFERENCE ON

# Physiology of Insect Development

HELD AUGUST 14–16, 1956

AT

MACDONALD COLLEGE

Ste. Anne de Bellevue, Quebec, Canada

*Conference chairman*
MAX F. DAY
*Commonwealth Scientific and*
*Industrial Research Organization*
*Canberra, Australia*

*Reporter and editor*
FRANK L. CAMPBELL
*Division of Biology and Agriculture*
*National Academy of Sciences–National Research Council*
*Washington, D.C.*

*Participants:*

DOROTHY E. BLISS, *American Museum of Natural History, New York, New York*
DIETRICH BODENSTEIN, *National Heart Institute, City Hospital, Baltimore, Maryland*
DONALD H. BUCKLIN, *University of Wisconsin, Madison, Wisconsin*
J. G. CARLSON, *University of Tennessee, Knoxville, Tennessee*
E. W. CASPARI, *Wesleyan University, Middletown, Connecticut*
RUDOLF GEIGY, *Swiss Tropical Institute, Basel, Switzerland*
ERNST HADORN, *University of Zurich, Zurich, Switzerland*
PETER KARLSON, *Max-Planck Institute for Biochemistry, Munich, Germany*
A. D. LEES, *Cambridge University, Cambridge, England*
A. F. O'FARRELL, *University of New England, Armidale, Australia*
D. F. POULSON, *Yale University, New Haven, Connecticut*
M. T. M. RIZKI, *Reed College, Portland, Oregon*
JAMES H. SANG, *Poultry Research Center, Edinburgh, Scotland*
BERTA SCHARRER, *Albert Einstein College of Medicine, New York, New York*
HOWARD A. SCHNEIDERMAN, *Cornell University, Ithaca, New York*
C. H. WADDINGTON, *Institute of Animal Genetics, Edinburgh, Scotland*
V. B. WIGGLESWORTH, *University of Cambridge, Cambridge, England*
CARROLL M. WILLIAMS, *Harvard University, Cambridge, Massachusetts*
ALEXANDER WOLSKY, *Fordham University, New York, New York*
GERARD R. WYATT, *Harvard University, Cambridge, Massachusetts*

# Contents

# *Introduction*

The conference on the physiology of insect development, growth, and metamorphosis was the only one of the Developmental Biology Conference Series, 1956, to deal principally with one class of animals. It was not, however, intended to be an entomological conference but rather one that would pay particular attention to insects in relation to general problems of developmental biology. In his outline of the conference Paul Weiss, general chairman of the series, wrote as follows:

The key position that insects assume in the study of developmental biology is well illustrated by the fact that they have become favorite objects in the study of gene action in development (physiological genetics), of hormone effects on development, of nutrient and metabolic requirements for growth, etc. There is thus emerging from a variety of separate sources a common pool of information which deserves to be reviewed from a common platform, so that otherwise isolated facts and views may be cross-correlated, inconsistencies removed, old ideas reassessed and new ideas engendered, and the whole field be given further impetus toward more unified and concerted research efforts.

The present conference is intended to be a step in this direction. It will have achieved its purpose if at the end the participants depart with a sense that they have contributed, as well as received, such benefits as: a fresh exposition of the basic problems in the field; resolution of larger problems into tangible and practically approachable issues; clarification of concepts, terms and facts; identification of areas where information is lacking or inadequate; notions of how such areas could be profitably investigated; and so forth. It is to be expected that if, at such meeting, the morphologist, the geneticist, the biochemist, the cytologist, the embryologist, and the pathologist each gets a glimpse of the interest, concepts and working tools of the others, they all will then return to their specialties with a broadened perspective and better common orientation.

Aside from such potential gains for the field of insect development as such, a major gain to developmental biology as a whole could come from a comparative consideration of insects in relation to other forms. This could point up the types of problems for the investigation of which insects would seem to offer uniquely favorable conditions, as well as instances of fundamental discrepancies between insects and other forms in matters of growth, differentiation and morphogenesis that could lead to improved insight into the nature of these processes.

Few if any of the participants would call themselves entomologists or even insect physiologists, but nearly all had used insects in their investigations, and many had become well known for their studies on particular species of insects. What they had to say during the conference was recorded on magnetic tape, monitored by Dr. Russell B. Stevens. The following report of the conference is based upon this tape recording; indeed, it is the only report of a conference of the series to be published in dialogue form. Its preparation was begun by Chairman Max Day, who dictated to a wire recorder what he heard on the tape. His typed dictation was then sent to the participants, who were encouraged to correct or modify their alleged remarks as they saw fit. Their excellent co-operation led to the typing of a revised copy. As Dr. Day was then returning to Australia, the revision was edited for internal scientific consistency by Dr. Dietrich Bodenstein, who also provided a bibliography for students. Excessive verbiage characteristic of dialogue was pruned out by the writer, and finally the edited manuscript was reviewed by Dr. Paul Weiss. To all who helped, including his wife, the writer is most grateful.

FRANK L. CAMPBELL

## · I ·

## *First Session on Embryology*

---

DAY (*presiding*): All of us appreciate that insects provide exceptional material for the study of many aspects of growth and development. They are particularly amenable to operative, transplantative, and parabiotic techniques, are readily available, and have a metamorphosis which provides a multitude of interesting problems in development. At the same time, there are many differences between morphogenetic problems in insects and vertebrates. It seems probable, therefore, that entomology can offer much to advance morphogenetic concepts and likewise can gain much from current thought in studies on vertebrates.

This is, I think, the main reason for our coming together. I should like to point out that this is the only conference of this developmental biology conference series which deals exclusively with invertebrates. In fact, it is the only conference of the series circumscribed by taxonomic limits. This is important. It is due in large part to the demonstration by many people, several of whom are fortunately here, that insects are convenient material which, in capable hands, may provide many answers to fundamental questions in biology.

One of my main concerns is that our information in this field (as, indeed, in so much of entomology) exhibits an extraordinarily uneven degree of development. Whole segments of our science are unknown, but in *Drosophila* genetics, for example, our knowledge is far ahead of most other groups. But one has the uneasy feeling that generalizations from one group to the next may be unwarranted. I hope that the results of the next three days will either dispel or substantiate this notion.

You will all have seen Dr. Weiss's "General Outline" for this series of conferences. In view of the peculiarities of our own problem, there are several aspects of these ideas which I should like to stress. You will have noted that the subject of endocrinology has not been given much emphasis in our outline. This is partly because there is a symposium on the subject at the forthcoming International Entomological Congress at Montreal but also because a great deal of attention has been paid to the subject. The hormonal aspects of insect development are, in fact, only

1

a small part of the whole subject. We might aim at restoring some of the balance of the subject of insect morphogenesis.

I think we all speak the same technical language, but there are among us biochemists, embryologists, geneticists, and physiologists, and each group has its own peculiar jargon. I would therefore encourage you to demand explanations and definitions of any speakers who get out of our common depth.

We have questions before us, but they are not agenda. Our aim is to discuss embryonic development today, larval development and problems of metamorphosis tomorrow, and abnormal development on the third day. These subjects are all interwoven. We shall not stay closely to any set program, but we should keep our remarks along these general lines.

The subjects which we hope to discuss this morning concern embryology, and I should like first to call on Dr. Wolsky, who will discuss some aspects of the early stages of fertilization in the egg, and then we shall hear from Dr. Waddington; but at any stage everybody must feel free to interrupt and ask questions for clarification.

CHANGES AT FERTILIZATION: $O_2$ CONSUMPTION AND RESISTANCE
TO POISONS OF THE RESPIRATORY ENZYME SYSTEM

WOLSKY: I shall speak on certain physiological changes that occur at fertilization in eggs of the silkworm, as measured by the intensity of oxygen consumption and by the resistance to poisons of the respiratory enzyme system. In the latest book of Rothschild on *Fertilization,* you will find little about insect eggs, because it is generally considered that they are not suitable for the study of the physiology of fertilization. True enough, one can never make such beautiful experiments with insect eggs as one can with eggs of various aquatic organisms. For example, the latter can be placed in a Warburg vessel and their respiration measured before fertilization; then the sperm can be added from a side chamber of the Warburg vessel and respiration measured after fertilization. The best you can do with insect eggs is to compare the respiration in a sample of unfertilized eggs with that of another sample of fertilized eggs. In the silkworm you can collect a number of unfertilized eggs immediately after oviposition by unmated females and make measurements fairly soon afterward. Then you can get another set of eggs immediately after oviposition by mated females and make measurements on these freshly fertilized eggs. Then the two sets of data can be compared. Results of experiments of this kind are given in Table 1. The difference is statistically significant and, I think, shows clearly that there is a certain increase in respiration at fertilization. I have also measured the respiration of both fertilized and unfertilized eggs at hourly intervals after they were laid, and I find no significant increase or decrease in respiration during the first 8 hours. Thus the respiratory level of the fertilized eggs is higher than that of unfertilized eggs not only immediately after fertilization but for some time thereafter.

The lower respiration before fertilization is insensitive to respiratory poisons, in particular to carbon monoxide. But carbon monoxide applied after fertilization inhibits respiration. Thus a definite change in the

TABLE 1

COMPARISON OF OXYGEN UPTAKE OF FERTILIZED AND UNFERTILIZED
EGGS OF THE MULBERRY SILKWORM (*Bombyx*)

| UNFERTILIZED EGGS | | FERTILIZED EGGS | | |
|---|---|---|---|---|
| Experiment | Oxygen Consumption (Cu Mm/Hr/ 500 Eggs) | Experiment | Oxygen Consumption (Cu Mm/Hr/ 500 Eggs) | Remarks |
| VII.20/B..... | 7.4 | X.10/A....... | 17.8 | |
| VII.28/I..... | 11.6 | X.11/A....... | 12.4 | Measured within 3 hours after fertilization |
| VIII.1/A...... | 9.7 | /1b........ | 7.3 | |
| /I | 8.1 | /2b........ | 28.7 | |
| VIII.9/A...... | 10.0 | /4......... | 16.4 | |
| /I........ | 10.0 | VII.18/2...... | 17.8 | |
| VII.10/II..... | 6.5 | X.26/A | 12.1 | |
| VII.13/IV.... | 7.7 | /1........ | 14.8 | Measured within 6 hours after fertilization |
| VII.14/B..... | 7.4 | /2........ | 12.8 | |
| /II...... | 7.1 | /1b....... | 8.4 | |
| VII.19/2...... | 7.3 | X.27/B..... | 14.3 | |
| /II........ | 7.9 | XI.2/1....... | 19.3 | |
| Mean and standard error.... | 8.4±0.45 | Mean and standard error...... | 15.2±1.59 | |
| | | Difference and its standard error=6.8±1.65 | | |

mechanism of respiration occurs at fertilization. Now we know that when the eggs enter diapause, which occurs about a day or so after fertilization, their respiration again returns to the prefertilization level. At the same time it again becomes insensitive to carbon monoxide. On the basis of these facts I offer the following hypothesis.

Let us assume that the total amount of cytochrome oxidase in the egg is the same before and after fertilization and that, before fertilization, only a small portion of the total amount is used and after fertilization a larger portion. Now carbon monoxide inhibits only a certain portion of the total enzyme, but the same amount both before and after fertiliza-

3

tion. Since only a small portion of the total cytochrome oxidase is used before fertilization, sufficient enzyme remains in the system, even after partial inhibition, to support respiration. Thus no inhibition in the $O_2$ uptake is noted. The situation is different after fertilization, when a larger portion of the total enzyme is used. Here the same carbon monoxide inhibition leaves not enough enzyme for normal respiration, and the inhibition becomes noticeable.

This hypothesis is supported by my measurements of respiration of the eggs of silkworms before and after exposure to a 10 per cent solution of hydrochloric acid. This treatment, as used by Acqua and Pigorini, has the practical effect of eliminating diapause and producing another generation in the same season—a "bivoltinization," as silkworm breeders call it. I find that this treatment increases the respiration of these eggs. Now in combining these experiments with carbon monoxide treatment, I find that a certain carbon monoxide–oxygen mixture inhibits respiration less in untreated than in hydrochloric acid–treated eggs. A small amount of inhibition is obtained in eggs before bivoltinization. But if one increases the respiration by bivoltinization, the effect of carbon monoxide at once increases also, simply because, according to the hypothesis, a larger amount of the available cytochrome oxidase is used for respiration and the effect of carbon monoxide will immediately be more noticeable. This is a very crude hypothesis, and further experiments are needed to check it.

CASPARI: Do the changes in respiration observed after fertilization have to be attributed to fertilization, or may they not be simply connected with the processes of development? Comparison of fertilized and parthenogenetic eggs—for instance, in Hymenoptera—would make it possible to decide this question.

SCHNEIDERMAN: One question about carbon monoxide: If I understand it, carbon monoxide combines only with the reduced form of cytochrome oxidase. That is, it will combine with cytochrome oxidase only after it has accepted electrons. This means that carbon monoxide will never combine with an inactive cytochrome oxidase molecule, only with one that is functioning. And even if you have a great excess of cytochrome oxidase over the other components of the system, one would suspect that you would still get an inhibition of respiration regardless of the excess, since the enzyme will be inhibited only when it is actually working; this problem has bothered us also.

WOLSKY: If the active cytochrome oxidase is blocked by carbon monoxide, I wonder whether the inactive part gets into action to maintain respiration.

4

KARLSON: At any rate, the action must obey the mass-action law. That is, if you increase the partial pressure of carbon monoxide, you will achieve a greater blocking of the cytochrome oxidase system. Are there any experiments in this direction?

WOLSKY: Yes, the figures agree quite well with Warburg's partition equation, that is, if you use a higher concentration of carbon monoxide, you get a stronger inhibition.

WILLIAMS: What happens if you give the hydrochloric acid treatment to unfertilized eggs?

WOLSKY: You get a certain increase in respiration which is similar to the effect of fertilization, and at once you can inhibit the respiration with carbon monoxide, which you cannot achieve on untreated unfertilized eggs. Thus the act of fertilization changes the system in a way that you can duplicate by this treatment.

BODENSTEIN: At what stage of development exactly are the youngest fertilized, the 10-hour old, and the diapausing eggs?

WOLSKY: The youngest eggs probably are at very early stages. Studies of Bataillon and Tchou-Su show that the pronuclei are not yet fused at the time when these eggs are laid. At 10 hours they would be approximately at an early blastoderm stage; the nuclei are just migrating into the periplasm. Diapause starts in some of them, let us say, in 24 hours, and by that time the germ layers are differentiated. My hypothesis is based mainly on experiments and considerations concerning the situation immediately before and after fertilization. The analogy with diapause and non-diapause stages is valid only if we assume that the increase in cell number and amount of living matter during these stages does not change the quantitative relationship of the components of the respiratory enzyme system.

WILLIAMS: This theory presupposes that at all stages there is a great excess of cytochrome oxidase. Perhaps it is fertilization that changes things. Perhaps one gets a manufacture of mitochondria and so on. Now is anything known about the ultrastructure of this egg, or does the yolk completely mess up this prospect?

WOLSKY: Centrifuging the egg very strongly reduces the level of respiration, which means that, by disrupting the submicroscopic structure, you separate the components of the system from one another. The active particles containing the cytochrome oxidase seem to be in the sedimentable fraction.

WILLIAMS: How about the ultrastructure? Is there, in point of fact, a lot of cytochrome oxidase present in the egg?

WOLSKY: I have not investigated this problem, but I have been trying to locate RNA, which is supposed to be in the same sedimentable particles as cytochrome oxidase.

BUCKLIN: Dr. Wolsky mentioned this possible change in the ultrastructure of the silkworm egg. The diapausing *Melanoplus* egg, as worked out by Bodine and others, is, of course, very similar to this in changes in activity of the cytochrome system. And we have recently looked at the changes in mitochondria on the inception of postdiapause development and find that the mitochondria stain quite differently in diapause than they do in the postdiapause embryo. We have used Janus green and also an acid green–fuchsin technique and find that the mitochondria in postdiapausing embryos take a heavy stain, whereas those in diapausing embryos we at first thought were absent, but later we found that they took a very light stain. There may be other differences between postdiapause and diapause mitochondria which we are now looking at. This would indicate again that there was some structural basis for the change in enzyme activity between diapause and postdiapause.

Also, the change in the *Melanoplus* mitochondria is a very rapid one. It occurs within an hour after a chilled embryo is brought out to 25° and will be followed, as you know, within a few more hours by the inception of mitotic activity and, of course, morphogenesis. It is also possible to terminate the diapause by explantation. And in such explanted embryos, one sees the same changes in mitochondria, in this case within $\frac{1}{2}$ hour after explantation. If one fixes embryos within 30 seconds after removal from the egg, mitochondria are barely stainable, but if one fixes embryos $\frac{1}{2}$ hour after explantation—removal from the egg, that is, and explantation to a hanging drop of Ringer—then, after that 30-minute interval, mitochondria have become strongly stainable. Now what the underlying changes are that are responsible for these differences in stainability is, of course, not known at the moment.

BODENSTEIN: At what stages do you do this? Do you always compare the same cells?

BUCKLIN: Yes, the changes which I mentioned all occurred in hypodermal cells. There are persistent mitochondrial staining bodies throughout diapause in certain cells, that is, in the vitellophage cell, in cells in the subesophageal gland, and perhaps in other localized cells, but throughout the hypodermal tissues and most other tissues of the embryo these differences show, and we compared corresponding regions.

CASPARI: In working with liver mitochondria in the mouse, I have become much impressed by the variability of these structures, in their morphological appearance, and in their biochemical composition and

6

function. Their shape varies under the influence of position in the liver, nutrition, poisons, and genetic factors. Concerning the remarks of Dr. Bucklin, I should like to add that I have frequently seen poor staining and apparently missing mitochondria. In view of the fact that mitochondria can change their shape considerably, from round or ovoid globules to filaments, the question might be considered whether in some cases they might not have become stretched so thin as to be beyond the range of resolution of the light microscope.

WIGGLESWORTH: I can perhaps defer a full discussion of this until we come to arrested development in the later stages, but I shall just mention now that I have been observing the mitochondria in arrested *Rhodnius* in later stages, when the growth is restored under the action of a hormone. The results agree exactly with what Dr. Bucklin has been saying and would fit in very well with what Dr. Wolsky has said.

SCHNEIDERMAN: What implications does this have on some of the respiration experiments on *Melanoplus* eggs? If, as you suggest, these embryos break diapause as soon as they are put in Ringer, then no one has really measured the respiration of isolated diapausing *Melanoplus* embryos.

BUCKLIN: These mitochondrial changes might indicate that there is a very rapid conversion, but this is obviously a rather premature hypothesis at the moment. But at least some change is indicated which is visible histologically within a very short time after the embryos are removed from the egg. Therefore, studies of isolated embryos should be made very soon after removal from the egg. There were indications in Bodine's studies, for instance, that explanted embryos acted less like diapause embryos than did diapause embryos *in ovo*.

WIGGLESWORTH: I have also been concerned with changes in the mitochondria following injury (I identify your explantation of the embryo with injury). Again one gets precisely these same changes.

BUCKLIN: The changes which we have shown in explanted embryos do not appear to be simply a result of the explantation, since similar changes occur in embryos which have been previously chilled. We already know that explanted embryos go ahead and develop normally—in fact, through to a hatching stage; so, although they are certainly in a somewhat injurious environment, it is not so injurious that they do not develop. Mitochondria of all animals are, of course, unstable and change their nature with almost any kind of treatment. The changes do occur with these explanted eggs, but, since similar changes occur *in ovo*, we felt that our changes were probably not the result of injury.

HADORN: In some vertebrate eggs you can injure the mitochondria

7

quite a bit and still have development. I wonder if anybody knows to what extent it is possible to dislocate the mitochondria in insect eggs and still have normal development. I am not well informed about this point. You can centrifuge insect eggs quite a bit and still have some normal development.

WADDINGTON: In the old centrifuge experiments by Pauli, the mitochondria must have redistributed throughout the whole internal contents of the egg and even in the cortex to some extent, and he obtained partial larvae, which contained normal cells.

SCHNEIDERMAN: But perhaps the insect egg will rearrange itself, as many eggs will, and the normal organization reassert itself.

WADDINGTON: In the strongest centrifugation, you have these partial larvae, so the rearrangement, if any, cannot have been complete.

SCHNEIDERMAN: If you injure the pupa of the *Cecropia* silkworm, then, within a day, carbon monoxide–sensitive respiration appears superimposed on the carbon monoxide–insensitive respiration of diapause. This suggests that there are changes in the mitochondria as a result of injury which bring about an increased saturation of cytochrome oxidase which is presumably bound to the mitochondria.

BUCKLIN:If chilled eggs were fixed and stained for mitochondria immediately after removal from the refrigerator, at what we call zero hours of postdiapause development, they showed poorly stainable mitochondria by both the stains which were used so far in this rather preliminary stage of the work. An hour later the mitochondria appeared stainable and looked identical from that point on, as far as we have gone in postdiapause development. For another week at least, they show no further changes except the possible increase in number later in development. The changes shown in such chilled eggs, in which the embryo was left in the egg until the time of fixation, were similar to those shown by explanted embryos.

WILLIAMS: The subject covered thus far points to the need for certain types of investigation which we might take note of. It seems that spectroscopic studies on these eggs and the embryos at the several stages are indicated. Also it seems clear that we need some thin-section studies for the electron microscope, to see actually what the mitochondria are doing. Here, once again, we need some more morphological and cytological information and some more biochemical information.

SCHARRER: Electron-microscope pictures of a variety of vertebrate tissues indicate that mitochondria are capable of considerable changes in morphology under different physiological conditions. I think that electron microscopy of insect eggs should be undertaken to clarify some of the points just discussed.

BUCKLIN: We are in the process of learning how to do this.

WIGGLESWORTH: We have some electron-microscope sections of *Rhodnius* which show these various changes quite clearly.

DAY: The point about the discussion so far which is particularly appealing is that we have brought together the cytochrome picture, the morphology of mitochondria, and the physiological work that Dr. Wolsky has been mentioning. It looks as though this is a very useful growing point, and some of Dr. Williams' suggestions might be appropriate. The fact is, however, that the insect egg is a pretty messy thing to deal with, and one must consider this in designing experiments to answer these questions.

SCHNEIDERMAN: Surely the embryo of *Melanoplus* is not too messy an object if you can see the changes in its mitochondria within an hour, and it should continue to be an appropriate object for study.

RIZKI: Working with the blood cells of *Drosophila* larvae, I noticed that hemolymph samples taken from larvae raised at room temperature always contained spherical intact blood cells. If you examine these hemolymph samples after 5 or 10 minutes, one type of cell (the crystal cells) can be seen disintegrating. But when larvae were raised in a cold room at low temperature and brought into the laboratory and in vitro blood samples were examined, all the cells began to degenerate very quickly. When cells are taken out of their normal environment or the native state, many things can happen before fixation is completed, and I have been wondering to what extent some of the structures that have been described are due to environmental alteration. How much of this kind of thing can take place in vertebrate mitochondria?

SCHARRER: Some electron-microscope studies were done with tissue culture material which seems to have been fixed very well. For some of these pictures where phase-contrast and electron microscopy of the same material were compared side by side, Dr. Rizki's objection does not hold.

POULSON: In Iowa this spring, Donald Ede made some preliminary electron-microscope studies on *Drosophila* eggs. In the micrographs that he obtained, there was little indication of mitochondria as they are ordinarily understood. This is a preliminary attempt, but it should be known that someone has begun to use the electron microscope on insect eggs. These were very early preblastoderm and a few early blastoderm stages.

WADDINGTON: First attempts have been made in my laboratory, too.

9

We are planning this very definitely in connection with one particular female sterile gene which I shall talk about later.

DAY: Since this subject is going to come up again when we talk about arrested development in postembryonic life, we might leave it now and come back to it later. Dr. Waddington, I wonder if you would like to show your film at this stage?

### THE EFFECT OF CERTAIN GENES ON BASIC EGG STRUCTURE IN *Drosophila*

WADDINGTON: I have been interested in the embryology of insects, not because they are insects, but from the angle of certain problems in general embryology. In particular, in the evolution of the animal kingdom the whole structure of the egg has completely changed. In the echinoderm egg there is a totally different type of causal setup from that in the amphibian egg, and the insect egg is still different. During evolution, therefore, there must be changes affecting not only the details of adult structure but the basic organization of the whole egg. We know almost nothing about the genes that do this or how they may enter into evolutionary selection. One of the few places where it struck me that you could investigate the genes which change the basic egg structure is, possibly, in *Drosophila,* where you have a number of such genes. They are called "female steriles" and are usually considered nasty things to work with. They are genes that cause the female to lay eggs which are abnormal in some way or another. We hoped that, by studying these, we might be able to find genes which caused the localization of cytoplasmic regions in the egg to be abnormal and thus cause an abnormal larva or embryo to be developed. That is, we have been looking at genes which change the basic organization of the egg: that was the stimulus that started us. We have examined a number of female sterile genes (they were studied by Dr. Sheila Counce). At the same time we have also investigated a number of genes which render abnormal the development of the egg containing them, that is, ordinary lethal genes causing the death of the embryo during the embryonic period. These have been studied by Dr. Donald Ede. We have perhaps not found a completely satisfactory case of what I was looking for—a gene which changes the pattern of localization of cytoplasmic regions in the egg, though I shall mention some that come near to it. But in a rather different way one can produce an effect which may be something of this kind. If you treat *Drosophila* eggs about 2 hours after laying, which is the early blastoderm stage, with ether vapor (we do not know exactly what the ether does), it causes the metathorax of the adult to develop in the form of

10

the mesothorax. Starting with an ordinary wild-stock *Drosophila,* I selected for the ability to respond to ether vapor by this sort of developmental abnormality, and after a large number of generations—about 30—finished up with a stock which spontaneously produces this "bithorax" type and gives these very large mesothoraxes in about 90 per cent of the individuals without any ether treatment being necessary. There is quite a different story about the changing of an acquired character into an inherited character, and I shall not go into that now; but the point for the present discussion is that one of the main things concerned in the genotype of the stock which produces this effect is a maternal effect gene; that is to say, females homozygous for it lay eggs which have a strong tendency to have this second mesothorax. That presumably means that the localization of the cytoplasmic regions in their eggs may be slightly abnormal, in such a way that you get an abnormally large segment where the metathorax ought to be. Anyway, that is one example of the general pattern of the body of the animal being controlled by genes working through the maternal ovary on the type of eggs produced by the female. I think that is probably as near as we have come to a case of a gene producing a change in the localization of the cytoplasmic regions and thus the fundamental pattern on which development is based. The other female sterile genes we have worked with are one called "Deep Orange," a gene called "Fused," and a third one called "Rudimentary." All females homozygous for Deep Orange produce an egg which goes wrong at the very beginning of development. In fact, the abnormalities occur in the swelling of the sperm-head nucleus, in the last maturation division, and the fusion of the two pronuclei, that is, right at the very beginning. In Fused, on the other hand, the abnormalities occur at the end of gastrulation, and there is a change in the morphogenetic movements of the egg that go on after gastrulation; in particular, the extension of the embryo that occurs at that time is abnormal, and this is followed by various malformations in later stages. In Rudimentary, again, females produce abnormal eggs, but the abnormality does not show up until later—between 13 and 16 hours of development, when the developmental processes which should go on at that time simply fail to occur.

The changes in Deep Orange are particularly interesting ones. A female homozygous for Deep Orange produces eggs in which the fusion of the pronuclei goes wrong if it is fertilized by a sperm carrying the mutant allele Deep Orange. (Deep Orange is on the X-chromosome.) The abnormalities occur in the maturation division and in the fusion of the pronuclei. But if the male has a normal allele of Deep Orange on

11

the chromosome, this comes in with the sperm which fertilizes the egg, and the egg carries on straight away, and things go right from this point onward. The Deep Orange normal allele must put things right almost immediately after entering the egg and even before it fuses with the female pronucleus. It is one of the quickest-acting genes that I have come across.

DAY: Does this mean that the chromosomes are acting before they have got out of the contracted form in which they are in the sperm head?

WADDINGTON: I should not really like to say that. It is rather difficult to say when the chromosomes actually appear in the *Drosophila* pronucleus. The gene certainly acts before the pronuclei fuse, for that fusion is often abnormal with the mutant sperm.

HADORN: That means that some product must diffuse during the period when the sperm nucleus swells. That would be the first instance of a very early action by a gene.

CASPARI: Evidence for very early action, about 8 minutes after fertilization, has been found by Glass and Plaine for the gene "Suppressor of Erupt."

WADDINGTON: It is the quickest-acting gene I know of. In mammals, when the sperm nucleus enters the egg, it absorbs a great deal from the cytoplasm. That can be shown by radioactive labeling of the egg cytoplasm; the sperm nucleus picks up as much label as the cytoplasm, as has been shown by Sirlin and Edwards in our laboratory.

WILLIAMS: This is a most attractive idea that the swelling of the protein is due to the production and release of gene products. It would seem an attractive idea to try to isolate the swollen nuclei and see what is there.

WADDINGTON: If you have an unlabeled sperm entering labeled cytoplasm, the sperm takes up a lot of stuff and builds it into insoluble protein, so the male pronucleus is taking substances out of the cytoplasm at the same time that it is bringing in substances.

As I said, this Deep Orange gene is obviously operating and producing something a very short time after it gets into the egg. This is a situation for which we badly want an electron microscope. The mutant egg, as you can see, has a highly abnormal cytoplasm, and the aggregation of plasm around the female nucleus looks abnormal; with the electron microscope, one might see what is really going on there.

There is one other thing to mention about Deep Orange, and that is the evidence that supernumerary sperm, which never unite with the female pronucleus, are playing a part. If you fertilize a Deep Orange egg with the Deep Orange wild-type allele, it develops all right, and this is brought about by the wild-type gene. If the same thing is fertilized by a Y-chromosome, it is going to develop into a male, and it has no normal allele of Deep Orange in it; nevertheless, it does considerably better than the homozygous Deep Orange. The only explanation we could offer is that you always have a number of sperm entering into the egg, and, if they come from a normal male, some of the supernumerary sperm will contain wild-type X-chromosomes; it looks as though these wild-type alleles in the supernumerary sperm do a bit of a job in making the cytoplasm normal. This goes so far that some of these males actually come to hatching and thus do considerably better than straight Deep Oranges. I do not know whether there is any evidence in other insects of supernumerary sperm actually playing a part in development.

BODENSTEIN: Can you tell how many supernumerary sperm enter?

WADDINGTON: Roughly, there are five to eight.

POULSON: In silver preparations the sperm tails show up. You can count them easily, so it is possible to get quantitative information.

WADDINGTON: It is only in the male embryo, which has no normal allele in its genotype, where the supernumerary sperm exert any noticeable effect.

## "NOTCH" DEFICIENCIES IN *Drosophila*

Waddington presented motion pictures, one on normal development and a second, shorter one, on abnormal development of some of the discussed female steriles and also various lethals.

POULSON: Is there any evidence for these being lethal in the sense of producing cell lethality in the ordinary course of embryogenesis? My recollection from Ede's paper and from looking at the films is that all the cells in these cases that we have just seen seem to be alive. What is involved is either a disturbance of morphogenetic movements or particular diversions of these movements. In the case of Deep Orange, of course, something happens before such later events can get under way, but there does not seem to be any evidence here that, so far as the embryo is concerned, these things are lethal, no evidence that they start to die. These and other genes have been called "lethals" simply because the organism which results eventually dies; but, so far as the life of cells is concerned, they are not really lethals at all. They are loci which intervene at particular moments in development, and this is why they are so significant to us.

WADDINGTON: I do not think there is any evidence that these genes kill off cells directly, though the Deep Orange effect would kill cells fairly rapidly by the disturbed cleavage mechanisms. It seems to act, in effect, largely on centrioles or spindles, and no cells would be able to survive it through many divisions. But these genes are not lethal in the sense that they produce lethal biochemical alterations. These are just genes which happen to cause abnormal effects in the early embryo and thus cause the death of the organism.

POULSON: There are cases in which the genetic changes affect properties of cells in a cytological sense. Things of this sort have been studied much more in maize and in other plants than in *Drosophila*. Beadle, many years ago, found mutants which affected the number of mitotic divisions and things of this sort and which made the chromosomes sticky. Recently a case has been studied in *Drosophila* in which a particular chromosomal deficiency results in a change in the cytological characteristics of the nucleus, particularly of chromosomes on the mitotic spindle. This is the case of the "vestigial" deficiency described by Dr. Alice Bull. In the homozygotes, as early as she could obtain good preparations of cleavage, the chromosomes are sticky and give persistent bridges in the developing embryo. This does not seem to interfere with the continuation of mitosis, but later on, after 10 or 12 hours, when mitotic activity normally declines, the cells begin to become pyknotic and subsequently die. This is a rather special situation such as might be expected when a gene change or loss is one that affects the functional activities of a localized part of the cell. It seems that cases of this kind need to be looked for, and we are actively engaged in searching for lethals and deficiencies with this in view.

Now let me draw attention to a case with which many of you are familiar but which others may not know about, the case of the so-called "Notch" deficiencies in *Drosophila*. Notch was one of the earliest known lethals. One of the interesting things that turned out in the study of Notches was that the effects could be localized very closely to a single band and presumably within that single band of the salivary gland X-chromosome. All Notch deficiencies which I have investigated so far show precisely the same pattern of development. It is interesting that the residual genotype, so far as investigated, does not have much effect. The embryological pattern does not seem to be modified by changes in the genetic background. Perhaps this has not been tried persistently enough, but the pattern is remarkably uniform. The thing to stress is that the change which takes place in these particular embryos is, as nearly as one can see at the present moment, in descriptive terms essentially a simple one. It is that whole areas which normally give rise to just a few neuroblast cells proceed to turn almost completely into

14

neuroblast cells. Thus in embryos carrying the Notch deficiency, all the mid-ventral ectoderm cells and all the cells of the head region of the embryo, aside from a small stomodeal plate, differentiate as neuroblasts. There are just no skin cells in those regions. The cells immediately lateral to these—cells which normally give rise to the tracheal pits and the lateral and dorsal hypoderm—go ahead and develop into skin and trachea. It looks as if a shift in normal localization is involved. At the moment there is no more basic explanation than this genetic-morphological one, although there do appear to be some differences in the staining properties of the ventral cells, suggesting that perhaps there has been a shift in RNA in cytoplasm. How can we account for this profound change in determination? Most of the other later features which have been described in previous accounts of Notch embryos can be given a rather simple explanation in terms of these early changes. Quite a lot of these later complications are due to secondary pleiotropy.

The earliest disturbances of development that have been found in Notch embryos go back to the time at which the gastrulatory movements are under way. Then one finds in the lateral regions which will become brain in normal embryos, as well as in Notch embryos, that there are lateral neuroblasts which literally come out on the surface and behave totally differently from any other neuroblasts which appear subsequently. There are a few others, which do not show at this level, symmetrically arranged approximately in positions which correspond to the original subdivisions of the brain. Some of these simply remain at the surface, although many of them move internally. This phenomenon of superficial neuroblasts is found throughout the head region in slightly older stages in Notches. Subsequently, neuroblast formation proceeds along the ventral line. In a sense you might almost say the whole neural area in Notch embryos behaves like the brain lobes. By counting the number of cells, it is possible to distinguish clearly between Notch and normals and to show that a far larger region of the brain is involved, even at this stage, in the Notch than in the normal.

A further feature of the Notches is of considerable interest in relation to problems of determination. In the later stages of gastrulation, as Dr. Waddington pointed out, most of the pole cells are moved into the posterior invagination of the mid-gut. Some of the pole cells had previously migrated back into the embryo, and I believe that the evidence indicates, although it by no means proves, that these early-migrating pole cells are the ones that become the gonads. The other cells end up as a part of the middle mid-gut section in the normal *Drosophila* embryo. Now the particularly remarkable thing that is worth emphasizing here is that in the

15

Notch embryos the pole cells, which lie in the mid-gut invagination between about 6 and 7 hours, are observed to do something which normal cells do not do at this time. They undergo mitosis. This is perhaps not so remarkable, but if you look closely at these mitoses, you find that cytokinesis is unequal and that these pole cells are dividing like neuroblasts, the only cells that divide unequally in insect embryos. This unequal division is a valuable criterion. In sections of the normal embryo, 6 hours old, the stomodeum is well defined, and the pole cells can be seen inside the mid-gut rudiment. In a frontal section at about 10 hours, one finds that a group of pole cells associated with the mid-gut come to lie in position between the two rudiments which come together. Ventrally there is a row of internal neuroblasts which will give rise to the ventral position of the central nervous system. The brain neuroblasts do not show in a median section. Close inspection reveals some supernumerary sperm tails still present. In a section of the Notch embryo, one can see quite clearly a neuroblast dividing at the surface. The brain region is practically all neuroblast. A cross-section of the ventral region of a Notch embryo shows quite clearly the area which has become entirely neural. This is the pattern that results from the loss of this one locus. Characteristic neuroblast divisions at the surface do not occur in normal embryos at all.

Below in this same preparation are several pole cells which were outside the mid-gut from the beginning and which are presumably the ones that will go into the gonad. These do not undergo division during this period. Only the pole cells that lie within the mid-gut rudiment show this unusual behavior in Notch embryos. In this embryo it is possible to count the germinal cells and to show that the number corresponds closely to the number entering the gonads and that only the pole cells in the gut are undergoing division.

BODENSTEIN: How long do they stay in this stage?

POULSON: One finds this happening only in the period of maximal mitotic activity of the ventral neuroblasts, which is $5\frac{1}{2}$–$7\frac{1}{2}$ hours. After this, mitosis is less frequent. Subsequently, you do find a big neural mass associated with the gut in the posterior region of the embryo. Previously, it was not possible to account for this association with the gut. Presumably it arises from these neuroblasts. This has brought me to look into a problem that seems to have been entirely neglected in insect embryology. It is the question of the origin of the neural material associated with the posterior portion of the gut. The stomodeal nervous system has been studied and observed in a number of forms, but I know of no account in the literature of the origin of the proctodeal nerv-

16

ous network. There are indications in these and in the control slides of the normal strain that a few cells among the posterior mid-gut cells do divide as neuroblasts. There are just a few of these, and presumably they give rise to the neural elements associated with the posterior part of the mid-gut and probably also of the hind-gut. One has to be very careful about interpretation of the material, but I think that the case of the Notch abnormalities has led us to a number of new facts which would not otherwise have been found out about the embryology of the nervous system.

CARLSON: Would you call the finally differentiated nerve cord of these embryos normal?

POULSON: The subsequent nerve cord in Notches is a kind of parody, if you like, of the normal.

WILLIAMS: In insects the sensory cell bodies lie in the periphery. Do they arise from neuroblasts out there?

POULSON: There must be isolated neuroblasts which normally give rise to the various sensory elements scattered all over and about the *Drosophila* in a variety of organs. It is entirely possible that all of them start to develop at once in a Notch embryo and thus contribute toward the enlarged nervous system.

BODENSTEIN: Do you mean that in these early stages the sensory neuroblasts are already segregated out and move to the appropriate places at the periphery?

POULSON: I think that this is probably true and that we have simply overlooked them because they are isolated cells. Unless you get a section in the right plane which shows one of them dividing as a typical neuroblast, you cannot recognize it as such. It will look like any other mitotic cell.

BODENSTEIN: Do they form connections to the central nervous system early or later?

POULSON: Early; otherwise how are we to account for the precision of connections? How do the connections between the nervous system and the periphery come about? A striking thing in the film was that in the early stages the nervous system extends the full length of the embryo in close association with hypoderm and mesoderm. Observations indicate that, as it shortens, the nerves in the various segmental regions are literally spun out, like unrolling a cable, as the central nervous system itself condenses. All the nerve fibers are stretched out from it while anchored to their end organs. The main segmental nerves are out in this relatively early stage. As the nervous system condenses, part of the decrease in volume is due to the fact that literally nothing remains but

17

the neurolemma containing the central cell bodies as the fibers are being pulled out.

WADDINGTON: Have you any pictures showing where the nerves from the imaginal buds arise?

POULSON: I have absolutely no information about them.

WADDINGTON: In the first-instar larvae the optic bud already has its connections with the brain.

POULSON: Yes, the optic bud already has its brain connection and presumably the main thoracic one also. I simply have not looked at this beyond the first 8 or 10 hours of larval life. You are simply pushing the problem a little further back, but one does get a mechanically satisfactory picture.

BODENSTEIN: But the impressive fact is that the peripheral ganglion cells are separated so very early, because one always thinks of them as later differentiation achievements.

POULSON: Yes, this is certainly the way it looks in this material.

WADDINGTON: Am I correct in saying that in one of Ede's mutants one sometimes gets effects like the so-called Notches, in that the nervous system develops very extensively; and in the same stocks there is the opposite effect, of too little nervous system and too much hypodermis? The fact is that you get both extremes produced by apparently the same gene, suggesting that you have some very subtle threshold involved.

POULSON: Yes, this would certainly appear to be the case.

WADDINGTON: In your work is it always an exaggeration of the nervous system and an underdevelopment of the hypodermis?

POULSON: Yes. In other words, essentially all the fore-gut and all the head hypoderm just never are formed. In the case of salivary glands, for instance, the cells which would normally become glands here become neuroblasts because of this one gene change. The whole of the material which normally gives rise to the imaginal discs of the head, the frontal sac, and so forth, becomes part of the brain structure. This is the way a Notch embryo looks in section. It is a Bodian preparation showing the gigantic nervous system. Anteriorly it appears to be all brain. When compared with the normal nervous system, it is found to have about two to three times the normal volume. The normal has skin, the salivary glands, and so forth, and the circumesophageal and commissural connectives are highly symmetrical. The connectives between the lobes of the brain apparently do not develop in the Notches, although the subesophageal ones are present. In sections of Notches and normals in more posterior regions you can see the very symmetrical arrangement of the bundles in the normal nerve cord compared with the rather asymmetrical and irregular ones in the Notch without any covering of skin. At certain levels in Notches, lateral bunches of neural tissues are present.

GEIGY: Are the gonads formed?

POULSON: Yes, perfectly normally and with about the number of germ cells which you would expect. Normally there are many more pole cells than actually end up in the gonads, anyway, and one of our problems was what happens to all these cells. If about 50 cells are produced and only 10 go into each gonad, what are the remainder for? I now believe that all the cells that go into the invagination of the mid-gut remain there and do not enter the gonads. Some of the pole cells, as Waddington pointed out, at the time they are dividing at the pole, remigrate in between blastoderm cells to become what everybody else has called "secondary yolk cells." I believe that these are the ones that go into the gonads. In the film at the time the pole cells became apparent at the posterior end, Dr. Waddington pointed out that some of the pole cells migrate back between the blastoderm cells into the interior of the egg. Initially, a number of nuclei enter the polar plasm. These then become cut off as pole cells and divide to give a large number of pole cells. Before all these divisions are complete, some of these cells just slide in between the blastoderm cells and come to lie inside. Subsequently, when the posterior invagination moves around dorsally, these cells remain in its vicinity, and they seem to be dragged along. They are not particularly conspicuous. They look rather like the yolk cells which are round about and, therefore, do not attract very much attention, particularly in iron hematoxylin preparations, where the very heavy staining of the yolk tends to conceal them. If you use Harris' hemalum or stains which do not color the yolk, then you can see these cells nicely. They are the cells that go into the gonads. This is what one finds in the embryology of other Diptera. In *Sciara* all the pole cells remigrate back into the interior at an early stage, and none of them goes into the posterior midgut. It seems to be only in those forms having supernumerary divisions that any of them go into the gut. Both Sheila Counce and I have been interested in the comparative embryology of a whole series of Diptera with respect to the fate of pole cells.

WILLIAMS: Where do these pole cells come from in the first place?

POULSON: They come from the first nuclei which happen to move out into the area of polar plasm, which has a lot of distinct granules that have been called "germ cell determinants." Nuclei isolated here become pole cells. The nuclei which do not reach this region remain and move about as you saw in the movie and then become either blastoderm or yolk nuclei. So you have the first differentiation, if you like, in the separation of several lines of cells. Subsequently, the pole cells become separated into the two, lines described before. The point here is that this requires extremely close timing. You have to watch a female lay an egg, then take the next one that she lays.

WILLIAMS: That cytoplasm looks like a good candidate for extraction, for an organizing principle might be found in the extract. It would also be nice if one could remove this region completely and see what happens. Perhaps one could do this by X-ray or UV. Dr. Hadorn's "Strahlenstichapparat" might be very useful for this kind of work.

HADORN: With our Strahlenstichapparat we can irradiate small spots of about 2 $\mu$ square. We have used it so far only for irradiating certain parts of the imaginal discs, in order to affect very small parts of the fields. We take the imaginal discs out and treat them in vitro, then we transplant them into the body cavity of host larvae.

GEIGY: There is one fact that is very unclear regarding the germ cells. I succeeded in killing them only before the arrival of the immigrant nuclei. After that period I could not get sterilization; and I should like to ask whether the larvae in these mutations are able to hatch.

POULSON: No, these are monsters. On the other hand, all cells and tissues are perfectly good and live for many hours. As nearly as one can tell, the gonads have a perfectly normal mesodermal coat. I have not attempted to take them out and implant them. Some years ago, Dr. Bodenstein did some implantations of Notch tissues for me. These were implanted into adult hosts and developed beautifully. We have only recently had the sections cut, but they are quite good and demonstrate the growth potential of Notch tissues.

GEIGY: But we do not know whether there is a connection between the number of ovary tubes in the female and the number of pole cells.

POULSON: This is at present unknown.

RIZKI: Coming back to the point of the effect of additional pole cells and their fate. Is it possible to take a count of all the sense organs? This number could turn out to be either the number that is missing from the pole cell count or a multiple of that number.

POULSON: I do not want to imply that pole cells which normally do not get here have anything to do with the normal sensory system of the larvae. It is only in the purely special situation in the Notch embryos that these become neuroblasts. This shows how far the determination of these cells can be pushed off the normal track.

WADDINGTON: Did you say that whenever you see a cell in unequal cell division you consider it a neuroblast? Are you justified in classifying them so or not? I am asking from ignorance. In insects unequal cell division occurs much more frequently than in other animal groups, and not only of neuroblasts but of cells which form all sorts of hypodermal structures at later stages.

POULSON: Fundamentally, these are probably neural elements. I just do not know whether there are cells other than those of the nervous system that divide unequally.

BODENSTEIN: Do you want to say only that in the normal early-stage embryo these are the only cells that have this unequal division?

POULSON: Yes; and there is one other thing that can be said about them. In normal embryos and in Notches, dividing hypoderm cells always have their spindles oriented in the plane of the surface, and this is true also of gut cells; in fact, everywhere you find mitoses, even in the invaginating mesoderm, you find the spindles oriented in the plane of the tissue surface. That seems to be a uniform rule; only the neuroblast divides with the spindle perpendicular and has a cleavage plane parallel to the surface. There are three characteristics: spindle orientation, the unequal division, and the fact that these cells usually tend to grow a little bit larger, which set them apart from others. There is some increase in basophilia during this period, which can be seen with proper staining controls.

HADORN: Are you quite happy about this unequal division?

POULSON: Only so far as cytokinesis is concerned. This is all in early stages, although I must say that I have observations on nervous systems of about 10 hours, in which some of the small ganglion cells are observed to undergo mitoses that appear to be equal. It is only the stem cell that repeats this unequal division. After the little cell is budded off, it undergoes equal mitotic division. At that time nothing is certain about its orientation.

WIGGLESWORTH: I wonder whether you have any ideas of the nature or cause of this excessive tendency to form neuroblasts? I like to think of differentiation as a tendency for certain cells, when developing certain characters, to appropriate the formative substances which are necessary for the differentiation of those particular elements by the gene system. According to this idea, your observations would result from an excessive availability of neuroblast-determining substance. Would you comment on this hypothesis?

POULSON: There is a difference in the staining of the material of the mesodermal rudiment in Notch embryos compared with normals. With hematoxylin it seems to be much less basophilic, and the lateral ecto-

21

derm cells appear more so. In normals there is no very striking difference in this respect, although, with toluidine blue, the inner layer is usually more basophilic than the outer. This staining is completely absent when sections have been pretreated with ribonuclease. As yet, no carefully timed series of Notch embryos treated in this way is available, but the material I do have suggests that the difference lies in RNA and that in Notch the situation is the reverse of what it is in normal embryos.

WADDINGTON: I should like to comment on this. There is this other gene which we have studied in which you sometimes get too much neuroblast and sometimes too little, and so, if it did not get too much neuroblast-determining material, it seems likely to be some slight shift in a balance which affects the situation one way or another rather than a gross overproduction of one substance or the other.

POULSON: As a concluding remark, in surveying all the different lethals that have so far been studied and analyzed, it is very interesting that not one of these that I have been talking about and which Dr. Waddington has described is identical with another. This is because development involves a composite of processes and fundamentally each one of these processes is unique. This suggests that we must look deeper before we can make sense of developmental processes in relation to genetic organization.

DAY: This illustrates as much as any other field that we are likely to cover just how much entomology can contribute to the whole field of morphogenesis.

# Second Session on Embryology

MOVEMENTS OF NUCLEI IN THE EGG

WILLIAMS (*presiding*): We have not exhausted the subject of this morning's session, particularly the questions "What are the mechanisms of nuclear movements and of movements of the embryo in the egg?" and "What contributions can genetic analysis make in answering the above questions?" I think we should inquire whether we can explain in any way the extraordinary motion of the nuclei and of the movements so clearly evident in *Drosophila*.

POULSON: As the first nucleus divides and this is repeated in subsequent cleavage nuclei, they move apart from one another in a regular manner. One gets the impression that there is real uniformity in the distance apart, but I do not know how to account for this in mechanical terms. There are insects in which the nuclei do tend to move to the surface in a sort of surface of themselves within the larger one. In *Drosophila* this is not the case, and the nuclei appear to be randomly distributed, although not strictly randomly because there is always a minimal distance between nuclei. There does seem to be an accumulation around the newly produced nuclei of cytoplasmic material which had been previously distributed throughout the yolk. But we do not know at all what initiates this movement; it occurs in *Drosophila* at a very specific stage, between the 256- and the 512-nuclei stage.

WADDINGTON: At this stage, it seems to me that there are two different problems, and the first is not quite so difficult as the second. The first is the general spreading of the nuclei throughout the whole mass of the egg. In some forms that Seidel worked with, you get the impression that the nuclei of each cleavage spindle are pushing away from one another, and this would give you the distribution through the mass of the egg. In some other insects, such as the bee, a second factor must be involved. This is a case in which the nuclei lie on a surface inside the egg; then you have to add the additional hypothesis that the cleavage spindles always lie tangential to this surface and that the daughter nuclei repel one another within this surface, which is parallel to the outer surface of the egg.

WILLIAMS: But are the nuclei being dragged by islands of cytoplasm, as Dr. Wigglesworth has suggested? Or do they have leverage to move themselves?

WADDINGTON: I think that the spindles would push them apart.

WILLIAMS: But this, as you suggest, would lead to an equal distribution of nuclei throughout the egg, and that is the reverse of what one finds.

WADDINGTON: Not if the spindles were in a plane parallel to the cortex. Then you would get them lying in a surface parallel to the cortex. Another point that one must also bring in is that those explanations would work for the first colonization, but then, when the nuclei move up into the blastoderm, they come very close to one another and are tightly packed, which is just the opposite of what they were doing earlier when they were repelling one another. Whether you must suppose that a totally different mechanism comes into play or whether what you see is a later stage of the same process, I am not clear, but I think there are probably several different processes involved.

BODENSTEIN: One should realize that the nuclei are connected by a cytoplasmic net to the periplasm. Therefore, a net contraction would move nuclear groups. A localized contraction may and apparently does result in a specific grouping of nuclei. Nuclear movement in such cases would be a passive movement.

WILLIAMS: One currently tends to emphasize chemical events, but surely there are a number of physical events going on in this developing system. Can we agree on what is leading and what is following in the motion of the nuclei to the periphery?

POULSON: But not all nuclei go to the surface. A considerable number of them remain centrally as vitellophages, or the yolk nuclei, and how these become separate, I do not know. Perhaps these are simply heavier or sluggish compared with those that reach the surface. Subsequently, yolk nuclei become endopolyploid. All the observations on these stages have been from fixed materials, sections and whole mounts. It is very difficult to distinguish much in the interior of living eggs at this stage.

WADDINGTON: I should imagine that they were all actually trying to get to the surface but that some get left behind when the surface is fully populated.

WIGGLESWORTH: It was Strasburger, I think, who suggested that since what moves ahead of the nucleus are recognizable particulates in the cytoplasm, there must be something which is moving the nucleus. Dr. Geigy's and other people's results have shown that the prime mover

24

in organization is in the plasma. That being so, one would suspect that the prime mover in this movement and concentration of plasma is the periplasm. At a certain age of development, that plasma pulls a lot of nuclei into its substance because it needs nuclei for further development, for administrative purposes, and for the supply of appropriate genes and gene products, and so on.

CASPARI: Strasburger interpreted these particulates as centrioles. It might be pointed out that centrioles possess a number of characteristics which would make them likely candidates for a prime mover, if such has to be assumed. They are cytoplasmic structures closely connected with the nuclear membrane, and they are in some way concerned with the formation of oriented and perhaps contractile fibrillar structures. I am not thinking of the mitotic spindle only, for centrioles seem also to be involved in the formation of flagella.

WADDINGTON: May I return to the remark about there being not only chemical but physical events going on? My impression would be that, by the time the blastoderm is formed in the *Drosophila* egg, there is much more definitely identifiable cytoplasm as distinct from the yolk than there was at the beginning, when the yolk and cytoplasm were more mixed up. It is very difficult to spot a piece of the newly fertilized egg and say, "This is non-nucleated cytoplasm"; but, by the time the nuclei have got to the surface, there has been some sorting out and formation of a layer of clear cytoplasm. That is the impression that one gets from sections, and that sort of process might play a considerable role in dragging the nuclei up to the surface.

BODENSTEIN: I have never seen a nucleus which was devoid of cytoplasm at any stage. There is always some island of cytoplasm around the nucleus. There is no such thing, I think, as purely nuclear movement. The term "nuclear movement" has become a figure of speech.

WADDINGTON: That is true, but when you have the four-nuclear stage, with clear cytoplasm around the nuclei, my impression is that you have much less than there is in the column of clear cytoplasm which you see around the blastoderm nuclei.

WILLIAMS: One should be able to quantify by explainable forces the movement of nuclei per se. Suppose they are all provided with the same charge; one could then conceive of a situation in which those nuclei repel one another and move centrifugally. Now the importance of this, it seems to me, as Wigglesworth has emphasized, is that the future fate of these nuclei is determined by the accidental circumstances of where they end out there. So we begin in shaping the future embryo in this centrifugal migration of nuclei, and that is crucial.

SCHNEIDERMAN: But in terms of prime movers, what you really need to ask, I think, is: Does the nucleus tell the cytoplasm "Go," or does the cytoplasm tell the nucleus "Come"? The evidence which Dr. Wigglesworth has mentioned indicates that the cytoplasm tells the nucleus to "come."

WILLIAMS: But I do believe that nature has been slow in learning how to push. Nature moves things by contraction, and so this would certainly suggest that there is a traction in cytoplasm. Now, if this is so, the only well-known system which contracts is the myosin-actomyosin system. Does anyone have any information as to whether there is myosin or any such system in the egg?

WADDINGTON: I think you have to take a wider view of intracellular movement. There is here pretty clear movement within a single undivided lump, before the blastoderm is formed and before there are cell boundaries. Consider cyclosis in a plant cell: if you have ever seen a film of that going on, you will remember how the whole contents of the cell, apart from the nucleus and the vacuole, are going round and round and you cannot see anything pulling or pushing; it is something concerned with chemical changes within the cell. Is it plausible to assume that the forces are exerted by definite structures? Rather, I think, it has something to do with the kind of phenomenon you see in a boat made from a walnut shell and camphor which acts by changing the surface tension of the water near it. One may have to take into account local changes in electrostatic attraction between one end of a mitochondrium and the things in its immediate neighborhood, and I think the forces involved may be very uncommon, kinds that one does not come across in any other context.

SCHNEIDERMAN: In amoebae I believe that myosin has been identified, and very likely in a variety of other situations where protoplasm moves, as in insect eggs, the myosin system will be demonstrated.

WILLIAMS: I should think it might be fruitful to look for genuine contractile mechanisms in the early egg of the insect. Something is evidently contracting and pulling the nuclei, and one could, with an adequate antiserum against myosin or actomyosin, perhaps discern it.

HADORN: I do not completely agree with your statement. Take, for instance, melanoblasts in vertebrates. They just move as single cells, and there is no contracting system outside the moving cells. Could not the nuclei with their cytoplasm in the insect egg behave like a small amoeba?

WILLIAMS: But it is not similar to the plasmodium, for we get disaggregation in this case. I should not be at all surprised to find an antigen corresponding to myosin in the insect egg. Consider Ebert's finding that myosin arises in each and every tissue during embryonic development and only later is segregated in its synthesis in muscular tissues. I think it would be interesting to test this possibility, and it could be done. Of course, if there is no contractile system, then we shall have to retreat to a Heilbrunn-type of mechanism, with calcium doing peculiar things and so on. If that is so, one ought to be able to interfere with it with agents that act on bivalent cations.

GEIGY: How do the germ cell nuclei penetrate into the polar plasm? You would think that they are forced to move to the surface and penetrate into the polar plasm, because, if you kill the polar plasm with ultraviolet, they still get into it, and there they die. They must be forced to go into this place and not into some other.

WILLIAMS: Not certain nuclei, but only the chance nuclei which get there.

GEIGY: But they cannot stay behind. They come perforce, and they die as soon as they enter the killed cytoplasm of the polar cells.

CARLSON: I should like to ask Dr. Geigy how he can be sure that the cytoplasm is dead at the time of movement of the polar cells. Death is a difficult term to define in this connection. Could not the ultraviolet radiation induce drastic alterations in the appearance of the cytoplasm from which it might subsequently recover?

GEIGY: The irradiated portion is partly extruded. Even with the nuclei in it, it becomes necrotic at once. It loses its initial fluidity, becomes very dense, and stains very darkly with hematoxylin. Finally, this material is pushed out of the blastoderm toward the posterior pole. The normal structure of the protoplasm is destroyed; there is no further development.

POULSON: Certain phenomena in unfertilized eggs of *Drosophila* may be of interest here. Changes that occur in the distribution of yolk and protoplasm may or may not have relevance to the early movements of nuclei, but it is very interesting that later you find furrows which are very like the cytoplasmic cleavage furrows of the blastoderm stage. The cytoplasm may become cut up into large numbers of small non-nucleated globules or droplets. In some places these are remarkably uniform and look like non-nucleated cells; in others they may be very large and would never be mistaken for cells. We are still in the process of looking systematically at the various stages of these bodies. They may have some relevance to the problem of what happens in the regular cleavage divisions.

WADDINGTON: In amphibian eggs you also can get what looks exactly

27

like cleavage furrows, with no nucleus. You can also, as Holtfreter showed, get great shiftings of whole masses of cytoplasm, and these move in a manner very similar to what happens in normal gastrulation. You get a pseudo-gastrulation in an unfertilized egg, suggesting that a lot of the movement is inherent in the cytoplasm. I did not know that the same interesting phenomena occur in *Drosophila*.

WILLIAMS: Returning to nuclear movement, I wonder whether anyone has any further thoughts on it? Consider that these nuclei go out and populate the periphery, but only those that land in the future germinal band make the embryo. The rest go on and make embryonic membranes and so on. Now what is it that determines where the germinal band will be formed? Is this on a predictable side of the egg? This seems to me to be a rather crucial question.

POULSON: In *Drosophila* and most Diptera, a rather large proportion of the blastoderm is embryonic, while in many other insects, particularly in primitive insects such as Orthoptera, etc., only a relatively small fraction is actually embryonic. The primary axis is established very early. At least in the insects which I know, the axis of the egg corresponds to the axis of the female.

BODENSTEIN: The cortical cytoplasm of some insect eggs already possesses a definite pattern, which is apparently laid down before fertilization. Thus specific cytoplasmic regions exist in the cortex. These determine the fate of the nuclei that move into them.

WILLIAMS: What is the essence of this pattern? There must be a mechanism underlying it. How can we interfere with it?

WIGGLESWORTH: Well, there is the polarity of the body. All the cells of the fully developed body have a polarity. When wound healing occurs, that polarity is retained, and when the female develops an egg, that polarity is transmitted to the egg, which at that stage is part of the female. I take it, Dr. Williams, that you are "trailing your coat" to draw out the geneticists who do not like these sorts of thoughts.

WILLIAMS: This is certainly a clear-cut instance of a cytoplasmic happening enforced by the maternal circumstances.

WADDINGTON: It was our idea to determine the nature of this cytoplasmic happening by studying the "female sterile" genes. It was changed in a rather irregular way in the female sterile genes that we could get, but I am sure that there must be others which cause more regular changes. There is a gene in *Drosophila*, studied by Dr. Auerbach, which changes the shape of the egg. In the normal-shaped egg, there must be a pattern in the cortical cytoplasm which causes the germ band to be formed at the right place. Now this mutant gene makes the egg shape very much more spheroidal, and yet it develops into a perfectly normal *Drosophila* larva and adult. Presumably the same sort of pattern in the cortex must be there but spread over a surface of a different shape. It is as though the cortical pattern is a sort of elastic bag distended by various amounts of contents.

BODENSTEIN: This is an interesting point. As Seidel has pointed out, it is the specialized architecture of the egg that provides the basis for the difference between regulative and mosaic development.

WADDINGTON: An egg in which most of the surface takes part in the formation of the embryo, as in *Drosophila,* seems invariably to be determinate, and eggs in which a small part of the surface forms the embryo seem to be more indeterminate.

SCHNEIDERMAN: One of the things we should like to do is to study the various stages of oögenesis immunologically and thus follow the appearance of the different kinds of proteins. Then, perhaps, you could state that determination at a certain level occurs at a time when a particular protein appears in this egg. This is accessible to experimentation.

HADORN: Nevertheless, you could not find the bridge to the morphology from this kind of chemical information.

WADDINGTON: The ideal experiment would be—if you could do it— during an early stage of oögenesis, to remove an egg from the ovariole and reverse it, that is, transplant it back to front. The cortical structure must be built up by the follicle cells lying immediately against it. The yolk can be seen pouring into the middle. You could show at what stage the follicle cells lay down the pattern.

WILLIAMS: It almost looks as if there is some crucial difference between the two sides of an ovariole. Here is an ovariole more or less loosely oriented in the body cavity, and somehow it is impressing a fundamental and crucial polarity on the embryo. There ought to be some difference, then, in the sides of the ovariole. Is there a polarity to the ovarioles?

RIZKI: Yes, in some cases the nurse cells are all accumulated in one part, and they send out these nutritive cords, which enter the maturing egg from one side only. One is placed where the micropile is formed.

WILLIAMS: That may be the crux of the matter: the position of the micropile determines the point of sperm entry. And if the Amphibia tell us anything, it is that the track of the entering sperm into the female pronucleus is meaningful. It may be that it is simply the position of the micropile as it is laid down in the ovary that is crucial.

HADORN: But the sperm is not necessary. In certain species of *Drosophila,* Stalker found parthenogenetic development.

WADDINGTON: There is a special body of cytoplasm underneath the micropile where the maturation divisions take place and where the pronuclei are formed. The point of sperm entry is a secondary consequence of where the micropile is and where the maturation cytoplasm is. As regards the point of sperm entry in the Amphibia, it is not nearly so important as people thought at first. The position of the amphibian organizer-region is determined much more by the primary animal-vegetative axis and where the yolk sits underneath the cortex. If you turn the egg upside down, the yolk streams down from the upper end, and you get the orientation of the embryo formed in conformity with the new position of the yolk. It seems to me that in the insects there is no difficulty in seeing how you get a polarity from one end of the egg to the other. It is formed in the ovariole. The primary oöcyte divisions give a number of nurse cells at one end, the ovum itself sitting down at the other end; and you have simply got a polarity from one end to the other. It is more difficult to see how you get the polarity which fixes which side is ventral and which is dorsal. It seems to me most probable that, in *Drosophila* at any rate, you have a bunch of ovarioles looking like a bunch of bananas; they are rather like this, with one side coming together to form the main duct. And, though I am not sure, I think the orientation of the ventral is inward and the dorsal side is always outward.

There is more to this than the straightforward orientation in the body. If you inject the ovary, as Hadorn has done, you get haphazard orientation in relation to the body as a whole, but you still have orientation in relation to the nurse cells in the oöcyte.

RIZKI: The only exception that I know of to orientation of the type which we have discussed I found in an embryo which was oriented in exactly the opposite direction—its posterior end was at the micropile and the anterior end at the other! This embryo was found at 18 hours, that is to say, the larva was completely formed. There was no chance of the embryo turning. This was the only specimen I found among some 24,000 embryos.

HADORN: Just this one might have turned!

WILLIAMS: We have been talking about a blastoderm and an embryonic axis, which are not completely understood. Next we must consider extraordinary shiftings of the developing embryo. I mean the movements that were so evident in Waddington's film. This goes even further, of course, in grasshoppers, where the embryo performs all kinds of complicated acrobatics, shifting all the way around through 360°. But there is enough here to concern us for the moment. Here is an early embryo, and now it undergoes these movements. How does it do these things? What is the prime mover, and what is being pulled around? Something is imparting energy to this constantly moving system, and from where is it being imparted?

WADDINGTON: Can one rule out unequal mitotic rates? In some embryos it seems that the movements are certainly not due to an uneven cleavage rate. There is no suggestion in *Drosophila* that unequal mitotic rates provide an explanation of the movements, as far as I know.

WILLIAMS: Surely the clearest case of a morphogenetic movement is in the involution of the amphibian embryo. Can anyone now state what is the prime mover there? There is energy involved, and there is a mechanism. Does anybody have any ideas about a new approach to the problem?

HADORN: Some experiments have been done by injecting different chemicals into the blastocoele of Amphibia in order to alter the internal pH. A theory put forward by Holtfreter assumes that the blastocoele fluid is more alkaline and that this pH condition changes the surface tension of the bordering cells and makes them move in.

WADDINGTON: I do not think much of the theory of changes in surface tension. The surfaces of these cells are certainly not liquid but have many of the properties of solids. Probably, for the amphibian egg, changes in the adhesiveness of the cell surfaces which give rise to tensions in the cell cortex, but not surface tensions in the usual sense. But though you can give a reasonable explanation for the Amphibia in terms of the tendency of some cells to increase their surface of mutual contact, I am not at all clear how it would apply to the insect egg. In the Amphibia you have large surfaces and large areas for the cells to move around in. In many of the insect eggs you are dealing with a very multicellular tissue with many small cells, most of which are directly in contact with other cells over their whole surface.

WILLIAMS: In the case of this extraordinary instance of blastokinesis in the grasshopper, does Dr. Bucklin have any ideas on this? How does it do this looping?

BUCKLIN: Slifer has studied this, of course, in eggs in which the chorion was removed and has watched blastokinesis. She has come to the conclusion that this is an active movement on the part of the embryo itself, not a contraction of membranes and not a contraction of the yolk system, but rather a sort of rolling movement in which the embryo contracts its lateral-dorsal walls and orients itself along the surfaces of the yolk. She finds cells which she believes are precursors of lateral abdominal muscle cells at this stage of blastokinesis and feels that these are the contractile elements. In isolated embryos I have the impression that the

31

laterodorsal closure may also participate and be an actively contracting membrane and help in this peristaltic movement of the dorsolateral walls. There the movement is, of course, on the gross level of the whole embryo. There are no well-differentiated muscles, but there are precursor cells which quite certainly will produce muscle cells. If you remove the embryo with its yolk from the egg, it does exactly the same as it would have done *in ovo*.

WIGGLESWORTH: As far as the general form of the animal is concerned, which is what we are really considering, I have a great deal of sympathy with the ideas to which Professor Hadorn was referring— throwing the problem back to the structure of the protein molecules, a chemical structure which would end in our regarding the organism as a giant molecule. I think that is a helpful way of looking at the problem, particularly when you are considering the cortex of the insect egg, for instance, in the non-cellular stage. When the insect becomes cellular, one has difficulty in thinking along those lines, because, although there are continua in the case of many cells—that is, continuous connections from cell to cell—yet you can dissociate cells, and they will reassociate themselves into the proper form of the organism. One of the classic examples, of course, is Bronsted's sponges which he puts through a filter, and they piece themselves together on the other side. What forces can be conceived of as being concerned there? If still hankering after chemical forces, could we not think of those forces as being of the antigen-antibody variety, highly specific reactions of cell surfaces? May we not think of such highly specific interactions as being responsible for these forces aligning cells? We know that particular epidermal cells will recognize other epidermal cells when they meet them and will line up with them. For instance, when an axon regenerates in the epidermis of *Rhodnius,* it wanders about indifferently until it meets another axon. It immediately recognizes the other axon, attaches itself to it, and follows it. May not such interactions be, as I suggest, of the antigen-antibody variety and be responsible for the sorting-out of tissues? In the speeded-up film, you saw those cells juggling around, and you can imagine that they were feeling for one another and settling down next to the cell which happened to have the right folding of its antigenic molecules to satisfy its antigenic requirements.

KARLSON: We always think of the antibody-antigen relationship as being of the positive-negative kind. If an axon meets an axon, it must feel related not as positive to negative but as something similar. We need another mechanism to account for the adhesion of cells.

WIGGLESWORTH: All that you require is a cement with a different charge perhaps. This is simply Linus Pauling applied to morphogenesis.

WADDINGTON: I have just come from Bar Harbor where a conference was largely devoted to the relation of immunological concepts to morphogenesis. Of course, there was a lot of discussion on the sorting-out of mixed sets of dissociated cells, how they find their like, and sometimes not only their like but other cells, such as matrix cells, with which they settle. The general feeling there was that one must be dealing with complementary factors but that there was no definite evidence that the complementariness was the same as the complementariness of antibody and antigen. The antibody-antigen relationship is one example of complementary things in biology, but this is another example which may or may not be closely related. A general point which is influencing ideas on morphogenesis very greatly is the existence of complementary surfaces of cells, so that certain cells stick together and others tend not to stick together. I think everyone will agree that that is one of the most important principles in morphogenetic thinking today.

WILLIAMS: The trouble with the forces that are known to the physicist is that they work only very close up and work inversely as sometimes the seventh power of the distance. And especially for van der Waals forces, you must be very close up; for electrostatic forces, not quite so close. We do not see about us an adequate physical chemistry to account for these happenings. And so we must presume that the stuff between cells is moving as Wigglesworth suggests, perhaps putting a kind of double lock on these cells. I am impressed with some of the thin sections of liver tissue which show them zipped together by little cytological knobs. This is the kind of model of an antigen-antibody interlacing in itself. But we have to evolve something at the megamolecular level or at the supermolecular level, to pull all these things together.

HADORN: We have direct evidence for this kind of interpretation. Many times it has been shown that certain cells like to stick together and that certain types of cells have the opposite tendency. Holtfreter called these phenomena "positive and negative affinities."

WILLIAMS: But I am impressed with the fact that cells can be dissociated by using certain reagents like trypsin or hyaluronidase, all of which seems again to point to a cement substance, as Wigglesworth has suggested. There seems to be some third component, some additional component, between the insect cells. It may be some kind of submicroscopic matrix. If it can be dissolved, then the cells will be dispersed. So, getting back to the movement of the nuclei, perhaps they repel one an-

33

other until they reach the periphery, and then a cement substance of some sort is elaborated to pin them together.

BODENSTEIN: Do you not think that the cement substance comes afterward? First of all, the cells must find out whether they belong together. The fact is that in a cell mixture a certain type of cell finds its own kind again. Once they are together, they can fuse by the cement substance, but this is secondary. The problem is how do they know that this is my brother, so to speak, and they only know it after they have come together.

WILLIAMS: This is a paradox it seems to me, because we have been thinking and following Wigglesworth's argument that similar cells compete and therefore that they should spread out and not try to occupy the same place. Yet we do see also that similar types of cells seem to like to get together and make a compact epithelium.

WADDINGTON: I should like to give an example of a tissue affinity in *Drosophila*. If a larval ovary is injected into another larva, it sometimes joins with the oviduct which is growing out from the genital disc, a very different disc, of course, from that from which the gonads develop. Normally you have two oviducts, each with an ovary attached. If, as a result of an injection, there are three ovaries, two of them may join one oviduct, while the third is attached to the other. But if on one side there is no ovary or it does not get attached, then the oviduct fails to grow out from the main stem of the vagina. You can sometimes get an ovarian graft lying very far anteriorly in the body of the larva, and the oviducts which grow out from this side are then very much longer and join with this ovarian graft. This was shown by Pantelouris in our laboratory. Much more often than can be attributed to chance, the ovarian graft joins with the oviduct, as if the ovary attracted the outgrowing oviduct. It not only causes the oviduct to grow out, which it would not otherwise do, but makes it grow out farther, as though in order to reach it. I mention this case because it seemed that it was time that we had a little direct evidence of these phenomena in insects.

RIZKI: It might help us here to think of the organism as a molecular continuum, as Professor Wigglesworth has once suggested, particularly in relation to plaque formation in *Rhodnius*.

WILLIAMS: I agree that the concept of the supermolecule is an interesting one worthy of our attention. But it is quite an extraordinary molecule which does things that molecules do not ordinarily do. Do you think of an organism as a sort of crystallization in a common molecular matrix?

WIGGLESWORTH: I say only that the mechanism has continuity. Characteristically, the organism is a continuum, and the only type of continuum that I can conceive is a chemical continuum. Now the simplest form of chemical continuum is a simple chemical molecule. The protein molecule is becoming a pretty complicated one, yet it is very simple as compared with an organism. When you get to a multicellular organism, it becomes to my mind impossible to conceive of a molecule of that type. But I am still trying to feel for a chemical continuity, and I can only find that in antibody-antigen interactions, which are chemical continuities, bound together by hydrogen bonds, by van der Waals forces, weak negative-positive interactions, and so forth. It is a chemical linkage of a weak sort.

WILLIAMS: I am willing to suggest an alternative type of continuity. That is the kind of continuity seen in a community. It seems to me that the growing organism, to use the words of Sherrington, is a kind of community of cellular lives. And I would extrapolate this to those kinds of communities that we understand and know about (at least sociologists think they do). We see there individuals behaving in an orderly way. We could not, I think, conceive of the termite nest or the beehive as a supermolecule. But it certainly can be conceived of as a community, and a superorganism, and a very orderly place. The trouble is that we do not see a basis of organization in the embryo in the same sense that we see it in a community of individuals with nervous systems.

SCHNEIDERMAN: But is the organization of the community of organisms not a chemical continuity? Are organisms not putting out chemical substances or ectohormones, and is this not exactly the same as substances being produced by cells in a community of cells?

WILLIAMS: What brings us together is chemical engineering!

WADDINGTON: Is the biological organism not a supramolecular structure and an infracommunity structure? That is to say, it occupies a level of its own and is neither the one nor the other of those below and above it.

WILLIAMS: That is the dilemma we are in; that is to say, we are both a chemical and a community.

GEIGY: If we could culture arthropod tissue in vitro, it would help greatly to elucidate these things—cultivate separate parts, perhaps join two parts, and so on. I know that this is a very difficult and important question, but this is a way for future advances in this problem.

### INSECT EMBRYO CULTURE

BUCKLIN: Since we have mentioned problems of insect tissue culture, perhaps it would be appropriate to discuss briefly our attempts to overcome some of the problems of insect embryo culture. While studying diapause in embryos of the grasshopper *Melanoplus differentialis*, we had occasion to remove embryos from the shell and "explant" them into hanging drops of insect Ringer solution. Some explanted embryos continue development in vitro to late stages.

We first explanted embryos at the twentieth day of the 38-day embryonic period. At this time the embryo is well differentiated; the body is segmented, the eyes are pigmented, the limbs are visible, and the embryo lies "on its back" with the incomplete dorsum open to the yolk. Several membranes surround the embryo and yolk: first the cellular serosa, then the cuticle layer of the shell (a serosal secretion), then a thin vitelline membrane, then the outermost covering, the chorion, secreted by the follicle cells of the ovary.

To explant such an embryo, we first dissolve away the chorion by immersing the egg in sodium hypochlorite solution, as described by Slifer. This procedure sterilizes the egg and simultaneously renders the embryo visible through the transparent vitelline membrane and cuticle, as shown in Plate I, *1*. We dissect off the cuticle and the adherent vitelline membrane, exposing the embryo and the yolk, inclosed by the cellular serosal membrane (*2*). Some yolk is lost during this dissection, and the serosa is ruptured, but it soon heals completely. Within a few days, the explanted embryo, still inclosed in the hanging drop, proceeds to revolve around the yolk mass in the striking movements of blastokinesis (*3*). It completes the blastokinetic revolution (*4*), engulfs the remaining yolk, and proceeds on the normal time schedule to the stage of hatching (*5*). The explanted embryos of *3*, *4*, and *5* are fairly normal in morphology, as can be seen by comparing them with the corresponding stages *in ovo*, shown in *6*, *7*, and *8*. The explanted embryos shed the embryonic cuticle and appear ready to hatch. Recently we have succeeded in "hatching" these explanted embryos by removing them from the drop, drying them off, and raising them in cages through the first nymphal instar.

BODENSTEIN: How old were the youngest stages you explanted, and did they develop to the hatching stage?

BUCKLIN: The earliest explants were 5 days old. At this stage the embryo is largely undifferentiated, consisting of a disc-shaped "germ band" lying on the surface of the yolk. Such embryos, explanted to hanging drops, elongate normally; develop typical segmentation in cephalic, thoracic, and abdominal regions; and produce the appendage buds typical of these regions. Development ceases at this point, probably because the embryo becomes detached from the yolk mass, curls

PLATE I

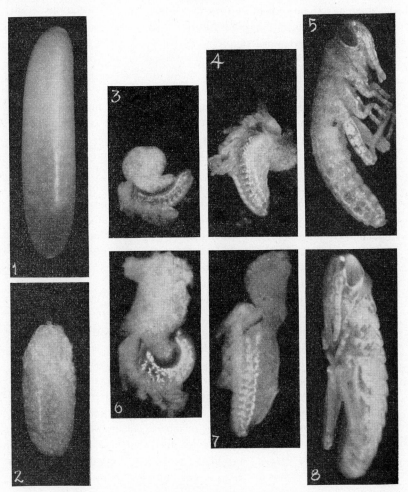

Photographs of normal and explanted embryos. *1* represents an egg at the 20-day stage, in which the chorion has been removed by sodium hypochlorite treatment, and *2* shows the embryo dissected out of the same egg. The embryo is largely obscured by the adherent yolk and inclosing serosal membrane. *3, 4,* and *5* show the further development of such an embryo after explantation to the hanging-drop culture. Compare with corresponding *in ovo* stages in *6, 7,* and *8*. Further explanation in text.

dorsad, and becomes abnormal in gross morphology. All embryos explanted during the first 16 days of the embryonic period failed to reach the stage of hatching, because they developed abnormal relations to the yolk mass, which is an important physical substratum for morphogenesis in the centrolecithal insect egg.

WADDINGTON: Must you dissect off the vitelline membrane, or do you have a chemical method of getting rid of it? It is a problem in *Drosophila*.

BUCKLIN: We have no solvent for that membrane, but we can avoid dissection. Routinely, we puncture the egg at the end opposite the embryo, which retracts from the tip of the egg. We cut off the cuticle and vitelline membrane at this tip and squeeze out the embryo with about two-thirds of the serosa intact.

WILLIAMS: This is obviously a technique of great promise. It is reminiscent of the kind of work that has gone on for some years on vertebrates at the Strangeways Laboratory. It may permit study of organ and embryo culture in a simplified situation. I am impressed by the possibility of using the embryo yolk in a saline medium as a source of nutrient for tissue culture preparations at later stages. If embryos can use it, perhaps the imaginal discs can use it.

HADORN: In respect to tissue culture in later stages, it is very difficult to have the right hormones present at the right time. Peter Demal from Louvain (Belgium) succeeded to a certain extent with discs of *Drosophila*. He certainly obtained further development in vitro.

SCHNEIDERMAN: There is little sustained cell multiplication. A Japanese (Kuroda) has done some work, in which the eyes of *Drosophila* certainly differentiated in vitro. This is probably a case of "momentum," that is, the continuation for a day or two of events already in progress.

SCHARRER: But if you can compare media, one in which differentiation occurs and one in which it does not, then that is very interesting.

WILLIAMS: The general question of tissue culture will be dealt with tomorrow. What can Dr. Hadorn now tell us about embryonic development?

HADORN: We made some studies of the biochemical changes during the embryonic development of *Drosophila*. My student Mrs. von der Crone-Gloor investigated the free amino acids. For a chromatogram we need about 50–100 eggs, which we simply crush on the starting point for a paper chromatogram. Then we determine the amount of the different amino acids and peptides present at different embryonic stages. It was found that the amount of glutamic and aspartic acids decreases very much during embryogenesis, whereas that of glutamine and αalanine increases parallel to the progressing embryonic differentiation. Most of the other amino acids show no striking concentration changes in the developing embryos.

WILLIAMS: How do you get the quantitative factor here?

HADORN: With the usual ninhydrin reaction and the Beckman technique. We do not hydrolyze our material; otherwise we would lose or conceal specific differences.

WILLIAMS: Then you get these contours descriptive of the normal, and you discern what the gene mutation does to it.

HADORN: Yes. I do not think it means too much. We simply make the statement that in a certain mutant we have at a certain period, for instance, less glutamine. It is analogous to finding a shorter leg in a certain mutant. Thus we simply collect facts.

SCHARRER: Do you establish the existence of mutants on such a basis where there are no other characteristics?

HADORN: No, we do not establish the existence of mutants on the basis of amino acid content, but we succeeded, for instance with pterines.

WYATT: In connection with these analyses I might mention very briefly some results that we obtained on the hemolymph of larvae. These were analyses of a series of stages of *Bombyx* during larval development and also a few samples from *Galleria,* the wax moth, and a few analyses from the pine sawfly. And in every case glutamine was characteristically one of the abundant amino acids. Glutamic acid, aspartic acid, and asparagine were scanty. Did you, Dr. Hadorn, find asparagine in your insects?

HADORN: Hardly any. It is difficult to be sure because it occupies the same position as others on the paper. The partition system we use— propanol and phenol—is, I think, the best for this kind of work. I should like to add that insects are very good material for the study of free amino acids, which are present in much higher concentration per cell than, for instance, in vertebrates.

WYATT: We determined asparagine quantitatively by the increase in aspartic acid after a short hydrolysis. The proportions of some eighteen amino acids that we have determined seemed to be characteristic of the species of insect, but how far this is genetically determined and how far it is a product of the particular food of the species is hard to say.

WILLIAMS: This is most interesting indeed. Florkin likewise has important new information on amino acids, using the microbiological assay method.

WYATT: But he hydrolyzes everything and loses his glutamine and asparagine.

### EMBRYOLOGICAL DEVELOPMENT OF NEUROBLASTS

WILLIAMS: Now Dr. Carlson has some information on the embryological development of neuroblasts.

CARLSON: Dr. Poulson talked this morning about neuroblasts of *Drosophila,* their precursors, and factors affecting the number of neuroblasts. I wish to talk about grasshopper neuroblasts and their divisions. My studies have been based largely on living cells in hanging drops of

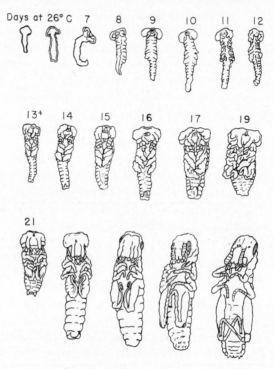

FIG. 1.—Stages in the early embryonic development of *Chortophaga viridifasciata*

physiological salt solution. I have used grasshopper embryos, *Chortophaga viridifasciata,* about 14 days old at 26° C. (Fig. 1). That represents about a third of development, from egg laying to hatching. At this time the neuroblasts in the thoracic region are at their best for cytological studies. They are large and are dividing rapidly. Before this they are quite small and very susceptible to osmotic changes. After this they are covered by the overlying layers of cells which grow posteriorly from the head region. Figure 2 represents the mitotic cycle of these cells and shows in diagrammatic form the asymmetry of the neuroblast that leads eventually to the unequalness of cytokinesis. There is a very distinct polarity to these cells throughout the divisions; the cells on the upper right, for example, are more or less concavo-convex, with the concave side down, and that is the side where the ganglion cell will form. The cell becomes spherical late in prophase. Then the nuclear membrane disappears, and the spindle begins to form. It appears to arise from the karyolymph, which flows from the nuclear periphery in-

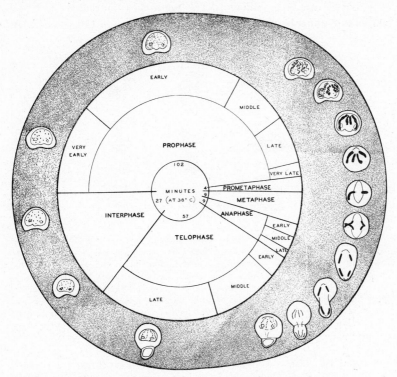

FIG. 2.—The mitotic cycle of the *Chortophaga* neuroblast

ward toward the center of the cell. At metaphase you will note that the spindle is in contact with the upper surface of the cell. This is a constant and very characteristic feature of this stage. One can predict from this that the ganglion cell will form on the opposite or lower side of this neuroblast. At anaphase the whole spindle moves downward, so that it loses contact with the upper surface of this cell and makes contact with the lower surface. There is then a brief period when the distance between the poles increases and the distance between each pole and the adjacent centromeres becomes less as the daughter chromosomes move

41

toward the poles. The asymmetric character of the cell then becomes more exaggerated. The lower spindle pole maintains contact with the lower surface of the cell, and the upper one moves farther and farther from the surface. The cleavage furrow forms approximately midway between the poles of the spindle and deepens to virtual completion during telophase. You will notice the difference in the resulting daughter cells. The daughter neuroblast is large and the daughter ganglion cell small. The nuclei are quite different. The neuroblast nucleus is large. Its chromatin stains lightly. The nucleus of the ganglion cell is small, and

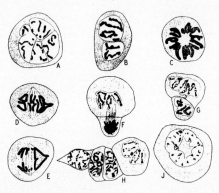

Fig. 3.—Characteristic neuroblast mitosis, showing representative stages and typical unequal division of the cytosome. These cells, which are from *Chorthippus longicornis*, differ from those of *Chortophaga viridifasciata* mainly in the presence of multiple chromosomes. *A*, middle prophase in polar view (optical section), chromosomes about to enter the prophase; *B*, late prophase in side view; *C*, metaphase; *D* and *E*, anaphases, in which only a few pairs of daughter chromosomes are shown; *F* and *G*, early telophases showing the inequality in size of daughter neuroblasts and daughter ganglion cells; *H*, late telophase in side view, showing a large neuroblast and three of the smaller ganglion cells derived from it; *J*, late telophase in polar view (optical section).

its chromatin stains heavily (Fig. 3, *F, G, H*). Very little cytoplasm is lost to the ganglion cell, so that the volume of the neuroblast cytoplasm changes very little with division. On the other hand, approximately half the nuclear material passes into the ganglion cell (Fig. 3, *G*). These are all early steps in differentiation. Subsequently, the ganglion cells send out processes that eventually develop into nerve fibers. These fibers become concentrated largely in the central region of the nerve cord.

We can interfere with early differentiation experimentally. Figure 4 (*A–E*) represents a neuroblast in which the division is equal. This can be induced in any of three ways.

1. If the cell is treated with 2250 A ultraviolet radiation, which is absorbed mainly by the proteins of the cell, the spindle is partially de-

stroyed, or its formation is upset. Such a metaphase spindle is abnormally small and is situated in the middle of the cell. It maintains symmetrical relations with the whole cell, and the cleavage furrow forms near the equator of the cell. After that, either of two events may occur. The cleavage furrow may cut all the way through, approximately at the middle of the interzonal region, and divide the cell into two equal daughter cells, each having the characteristics of the mother neuroblast. Or, as sometimes happens late in division, a pseudopod-like formation may project out from one side, into which much protoplasm flows, and the cleavage furrow shifts somewhat (Fig. 4, *F*). When division is completed, there is a large cell and a small cell (Fig. 4, *G*). The former has a nucleus characteristic of the neuroblast and the latter a nucleus characteristic of a ganglion cell, and each is situated at the predetermined pole.

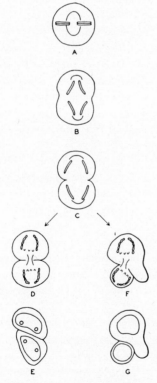

Fig. 4.—Diagram showing ultraviolet-induced abnormalities in mitosis of *Chortophaga*. *A–G*, treatment at late metaphase or early anaphase: spindle abnormally short (*A*), cleavage furrow appears at cell equator (*B, C*) to give a symmetrical division (*D, E*) or a secondarily produced asymmetrical division (*F, G*).

2. Colchicine acts in the same way, presumably through an effect primarily on the spindle. The colchicine concentration is very critical: $0.2 \times 10^{-6}\ M$ at pro-metaphase or $2.0 \times 10^{-6}\ M$ at metaphase.

3. If one inserts a microneedle into a neuroblast and holds the needle against the spindle so that it cannot shift position at anaphase as it normally does, the cleavage furrow, which forms approximately midway between the poles of the spindle, will be situated near the equator of the cell. The resulting two cells have the characteristics of neuroblasts.

The particular pole of the spindle or the particular set of daughter chromosomes that a daughter cell receives does not seem to determine whether it will end up a neuroblast or a ganglion cell. If one puts a microneedle into the neuroblast and rotates the spindle through 180° while the cell is undergoing anaphase, the positions of the daughter sets of chromosomes can be reversed end for end. Yet a typical neuroblast forms where a ganglion cell normally would have developed, even though the neuroblast received the chromosomes that would otherwise have moved into the ganglion cell and the ganglion cell those that would have entered the neuroblast. This shows definitely that this polarity is not dependent on the nuclear contents. If one rotates the spindle not through 180°, but through about 90°, cleavage is quite abnormal. First, a small indentation arises on the other side of the neuroblast opposite the group of ganglion cells. Then pseudopodia-like processes push out from the ganglion cell side, and the protoplasm becomes quite fluid. After an abnormal length of time, the chromosomes of each separating group fuse with one another, become highly refractile, and finally approach one another as a preliminary to the death of the cell. Cytokinesis fails to occur. Possibly this is related to the polarity of the neuroblasts; possibly it is due to the pressure of surrounding cells. Around the neuroblast there appears to be a cap of connective tissue cells inclosing the neuroblast except on the ganglion cell side, which is therefore the only place that a small projection representing the future ganglion cell can push out. When the spindle axis is rotated through 90°, anaphase elongation may be restricted by this cap of cells, and cleavage is incomplete or does not occur at all. I have inserted a needle between the neuroblast and this cap of cells and tried to pull the cap out to relieve the tension on one side, so that a small cell could form there, but so far this has not resulted.

WILLIAMS: What does all this mean in terms of the differentiative act?

CARLSON: I think in the grasshopper neuroblast (Fig. 5) and ganglion cell we have an example of a very conspicuous and, so to speak, sudden kind of differentiation. Many other sister cells in the embryo are probably unequal at a chemical level but not at a microscopic level. The neuroblast-ganglion cell system, I should say, is adapted to the laying-down of a large number of cells. The large neuroblasts, possibly by virtue of their large lobed nuclei and the retention in each division of most of the cytoplasm, divide relatively rapidly. Their fixed division polarity assures that the daughter ganglion cells will be laid down in regular rows.

SCHNEIDERMAN: I find it rather astounding that when you rotate the spindle 90° in a cell ready to divide, it suddenly stops dividing.

WILLIAMS: The nucleus does divide; it is the cytoplasm that does not.

BUCKLIN: Does it then go ahead and differentiate?

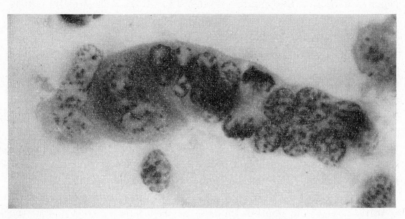

FIG. 5.—A *Chortophaga* neuroblast with its column of daughter ganglion cells, one of which is dividing.

CARLSON: I really have not been able to determine that. These experiments were done at room temperature, which fluctuated and is bad for these cells. They are very sensitive to osmotic pressure changes. Though you can keep a preparation going for 2 or 3 hours, that is not long enough to follow the differentiation.

WADDINGTON: Certain parts of the cell cortex are going to form a small ganglion cell when chromosomes are going to come into it, but if you rotate the spindle through 90°, the chromosomes do not come into it, and the thing flops. There is another case which Hörstadius has worked with in the formation of the micromeres in the echinoderms. The cleavage spindles go through a definite pattern of orientation, but, by altering the salt content of the sea water, one can change the time at which cell division occurs relative to the alterations in the spindle

45

orientations. Again you get the same general picture of the pattern of cytokinesis fixed in the cell cortex. A cell division takes place and affects the cortex at a given time, and one finds that it occurs in the form that that cortex is prepared to accept at that time.

SCHNEIDERMAN: I am not clear. Does the spindle finish its job?

CARLSON: The answer to this depends on what one considers to be the job of the spindle. If one considers its primary functions to consist of the metaphase orientation of the chromosomes and the initial movement of their halves toward the poles, as I do, it has completed its job. But if one considers it to be responsible for all the movement apart of the chromosome halves, then it has not completed its job.

O'FARRELL: From the slides, I got the impression that in those in which you rotated the spindle through 180° there was already a little stack of ganglion cells formed. What happens if you catch a neuroblast before there are any ganglion cells?

CARLSON: I have not tried this. Ganglion cell formation develops progressively from anterior to posterior, so that one can find neuroblasts with different numbers of ganglion cells. The largest neuroblasts with the most ganglion cells are anterior; they are smaller posteriorly and have formed fewer ganglion cells. One should, therefore, be able to find a ganglion cell without any daughter ganglion cells, but it would be a very small cell and hence a difficult one to experiment with. My impression is that when a neuroblast divides to form its first ganglion cell, it is not much bigger than the ganglion cell. Small cells are also more difficult to work with because they are very sensitive to osmotic pressure.

WILLIAMS: Could you kill the next adjacent ganglion cell so that the developing system would no longer be up against adult tissue? I got the impression here that there is some kind of determinative effect due to the presence of the adult tissue.

CARLSON: That raises the question of killing. You can do a lot to these cells experimentally, and you are never quite sure whether they are dead or not. Little damage is usually done to the neuroblast if the needle in it is moved quite slowly without any jerky motion. Once you jerk it or move it rapidly, the cytoplasm begins to liquefy, and the chromosomes become highly refractive and pyknotic. If one moved the needle back and forth through the ganglion cells in contact with a neuroblast, one could severely damage or kill them, but the remains of the ganglion cells would still be in contact with the neuroblast, and so the polarity might not be altered.

WILLIAMS: It would certainly be a good idea to try. It should be technically feasible to pin it up against the cover slip.

POULSON: By enzyme treatment, can you separate the ganglion cell from the neuroblast?

CARLSON: You can, but then rotating the spindle independently of the cell presents a problem. One might be able to cut through the thoracic region and locate a cell sticking out more or less by itself but still attached to the cut surface of the embryo. This might hold it in position during micromanipulation.

WIGGLESWORTH: If we accept Dr. Waddington's interpretation of the importance of the cortex of the cell, it is perhaps worth pointing out the obvious and extremely close similarity between this and the determination of nuclear fate in the plasma of mosaic eggs, which has exactly the same effect.

BODENSTEIN: Do ultraviolet-treated neuroblasts divide more than once?

CARLSON: I do not know. I have not attempted to follow them through more than one generation, but one might conceivably follow them through another division or two. Untreated neuroblasts can usually be followed through one complete cycle, often through two or three; then the divisions slow down. The second day at 38° C. there will not be so many, and the third day mitosis will almost have stopped. It would be interesting to know the future history of the two sister neuroblasts. Irradiated neuroblasts are certainly slowed down in the division in which they were treated, and I think that the division rate is retarded in subsequent cell generations. This increases the difficulties in following the irradiated cells through several divisions.

HADORN: Can you already see differences in the chromosomes at anaphase?

CARLSON: No, not until telophase, for we use as a criterion of telophase the time at which the neuroblast chromosomes begin to lose their sharp outlines. The ganglion cell chromosomes do not undergo this change until later.

WILLIAMS: That is a haploid cell which undergoes mitosis to produce two germ cells, one of which is male and the other female. But at the time of that mitotic division, Cleveland can see that the replicated chromosomes differ. That is a most astonishing case and points, I think, to a chromosomal basis for sexual differentiation. But Carlson's information must come as a blow to the geneticists.

CARLSON: You cannot, in either living or stained neuroblasts, see any difference between these sets of daughter chromosomes until the cleavage furrow is almost complete.

*Physiology of Insect Development*

CHEMICAL REVERSAL OF ACTION OF THE "BAR" GENE IN *Drosophila*

WILLIAMS: We shall now hear from Dr. Karlson. He has an interest in the action of chemicals which tend to reverse certain gene mutations.

KARLSON: Our work is related to the action of the "Bar" gene which causes the reduction of the eye size; the facet number may go down from 600 to 700 in the normal eye to 80–120 facets in the Bar eye. It is known from the work of Chevais and others that this effect can be reversed by some chemicals, methylhydantoin and creatinine being the most effective. We found the greatest activity in the excreta from the emerging adult moths of *Vanessa*. Apparently it is not a single substance but a mixture which gives the effect. This is compatible with the hypothesis that these substances are acting as vitamins, affecting the penetration of the gene; an analogy is the mutant "Antennaless," which is sensitive to riboflavin; a high dose of riboflavin in the medium totally suppresses the action of Antennaless, as found by Gordon and Sang, and you get perfectly normal flies. Perhaps we should discuss this question again in connection with nutrition and postembryonic development.

WILLIAMS: What are the compounds which you found most active as anti-Bar?

KARLSON: We have repeated the work of Chevais and found that methylhydantoin was active, but not so active in our experiments as he reported. Our extracts of *Vanessa* give a very clear response with only slightly higher dose; the active substances in the extract must, therefore, be different from methylhydantoin. We could not determine what they really are because the assay method in *Drosophila* was not good, the variation was very great, and the counting of the cells was very time-consuming.

HADORN: How do your treatments affect time of development?

KARLSON: That differs in different series. The time of development is prolonged in some series from 1 to 2 days. Some chemicals that we tried gave very poor development—e.g., cytosine and uracil, whose activity could not be determined with certainty. The 40-hour-old larvae feed continuously on food containing the substance to be tested. Is it the larval life which is prolonged? Pupal development is normal, so far as we have determined.

CASPARI: In this connection, Zalokar's recent work is pertinent. He had two strains of flies, one from Zurich and one from Geneva, which differed in the size of the Bar-eyes, when the gene Bar was introduced into these strains. Genetically, the difference turned out to be a complex polygenic effect. If flies from the two strains were investigated by paper chromatography, they turned out to differ in the size and intensity

48

of one fluorescent spot. If these spots were cut out and their eluted contents added to the food of Bar flies, a strong influence of this substance on the facet number of the Bar flies was found.

WADDINGTON: Kaje in Japan studied a large series of compounds containing acetamides, which were active as anti-Bar substances.

SANG: It may be worth mentioning that in the ordinary Bar cultures you do get a variability from day to day as the culture develops. The first flies show more Bar effect than those which come later. This again suggests a general nutritional effect, but it is very difficult to distinguish between this and delay in larval development, which is also effective.

KARLSON: In the most active extracts it cannot be the prolonged life which is responsible. These extracts give nearly normal developmental time and facet numbers of about 350. On the other hand, you can have poor development, prolonged larval life, and only a small effect on eye size.

WILLIAMS: But it certainly points to the need in the study of gene action for intervention with extrinsic chemicals. If the synthesis required an extract, then one ought to be able to tinker with it and influence gene action.

KARLSON: I should not like to say that we have a specific morphogenetic substance for those eyes. I should rather say that the gene action is somewhat altered by these extracts.

SANG: There is another point worth mentioning. When we are dealing with an insect like *Drosophila*, the pupal stage may have its own distinct range of homeostatic mechanisms, processes which will bring about adjustments of larval deficiencies and therefore act as a barrier between our examination of the effects of chemicals on gene action and our analysis of their phenotypic results in the adult. Very often these deficiencies cannot be overcome, and we are left with our viable larva turning into an inviable pupa with which we can do nothing. We tend to forget this screening process, which is the pupal instar and which limits what we can do with the holometabola.

WILLIAMS: Yes, this channelization of development is certainly a regulative thing inbuilt into the host to oppose anything we do. For present purposes, it is worth recalling that the genes in these metamorphosing insects not only build a larva but also have the responsibility of building the pupa and the adult. We shall hear more about the later embryology tomorrow.

# III

# Larval Development and Tissue Culture

FIELD ORGANIZATION OF THE IMAGINAL DISCS OF *Drosophila*

DAY (*presiding*): We are concerned this morning with larval development. We shall start with Dr. Hadorn, who has something to contribute on "fields" in the imaginal discs.

HADORN: I wish to discuss the field organization of the larval imaginal discs of *Drosophila*. Most, but not quite all, of the work has been published. We studied mainly the genital disc, which builds the whole internal and external genital apparatus (except the gonads) and the last abdominal segments. This disc is especially favorable for our studies because it forms a series of distinct elements, such as the sperm pumps, the claspers, the anal plates and the spermathecae in males, the vaginal and anal plates in females. For all these elements we can get exact quantitative data with respect to the degree of differentiation by simple measurements or by counting the bristles. We dissect the disc from donor larvae and cut it into different parts, which we then implant into other larvae, where they can develop during metamorphosis of the flies. Thereby these fragments of the discs show us their developmental capacities. We found, first, that the building materials of the different elemental organs (sperm pump, claspers, etc.) can be localized within the larval disc. A topographic map of the different organ-forming districts could be designed. These districts, or areas, form, as a whole, a mosaic in the old sense of experimental embryology. One never gets any overlapping regulation. Cells which lie outside the sperm-pump area cannot form this organ.

Each single area has, however, all the regulative qualities of an ideal embryonic field. If, for instance, we cut the sperm-pump field into two parts, each of the half-fields forms, as a transplant, a completely normal sperm pump of normal size. If we divide a disc into three fragments such that the two cuts run through the center of the bicentric anal-plate field, we shall obtain from each fragment two anal plates of normal size and unreduced bristle number. Thus, after cutting, the material of one disc now forms six anal plates, each with about 30 bristles, instead of two plates of the same size and with the same cell number which the uncut disc would have differentiated. We think that, after cutting, a restitution of the original field structure takes place in the separated parts and an increase in cells (mitosis) sets in until the original size of the field is restored. We never observed incomplete or undersized sperm pumps, claspers, or anal plates formed by fragments of discs. These regulative activities within the fields are real all-or-none effects.

By transplanting parts of female discs into hosts of different larval age, we found that the cases in which half a field forms two spermathecae (regulation) instead of only one (no regulation) increase with the time which elapses between the implantation and the onset of the host's metamorphosis. We explain this finding as follows: increase in the cells of the reduced field is a prerequisite for the all-or-none type of regulation. If a field fragment lies in an old host, which enters metamorphosis shortly after the implantation, then the cells must react suddenly to the metamorphosis hormones; they must differentiate before they have time to restore the necessary field size. In a younger host, in which metamorphosis begins only after 1 day, there is ample time for additional mitosis.

The results so far reported hold true for *Drosophila melanogaster*. We also did some work on *D. montium,* a species which differentiates a very distinct pattern, with four different types of bristles and thorns on the claspers. To our surprise, we found that, in this species, claspers of reduced size could be formed from small field fragments. Nevertheless, regulation takes place. All four types of bristles are present, and they are so arranged that a reduced, but complete, "image" of the complete field pattern is reproduced.

In still further experiments we were able to show that chemicals—i.e., colchicine, lithium salts, hypertonic and hypotonic solutions—alter or destroy the organization and developmental potencies of the field in the genital discs.

BODENSTEIN: If you transplant young discs into old animals, do you get a smaller plate in that case?

HADORN: No. In *D. melanogaster* we never get, for example, a small sperm pump. Each organ, if it is formed, is of normal size.

WADDINGTON: In "Bithorax," for instance, you get a mesothorax formed from the metathorax. In any Bithorax type you can get either a more or less full-sized Bithorax. In a smaller than normal mesothorax, all the bristles are complete, but much smaller.

HADORN: The work of E. B. Lewis has shown that the disc of the

Physiology of Insect Development

metathorax contains at least two fields which are controlled by different mutational sites (pseudoalleles).

WADDINGTON: In this case it is the anterior one that is formed. There are more than two, and it is a very complicated field. Lewis has obtained several genes which act on a number of different places, but in this stock it is mainly the anterior part of the mesothoracic field that is changed. To mention another case, in the duplications of the antenna you often get a reduction of the eye, but there you will notice the two antennae on one side are of full size, as in Hadorn's example, but in the Bithorax case the fields can get smaller.

DAY: Has anybody a suggestion about the difference here between the thoracic discs and the other discs?

WADDINGTON: I would suggest that the isolated parts are always, as it were, trying to get to full size, but sometimes the time is insufficient.

SCHARRER: It would look to me as though you implied, but did not have time to discuss in detail, that an enlargement or growth of the disc takes place in the host during the time when the growth and differentiating hormone is not yet present and that differentiation occurs as soon as this hormonal milieu is ready. Now does that not have a bearing upon the interpretation of the action of this hormone—let us call it "prothoracic gland hormone"? It does not simply allow, or have nothing to do with, differentiation, for in this experiment it would seem that it actually stimulates differentiation. I think that one can draw a conclusion as to the nature of this hormone. Before it is present, there is growth of the disc, and, after its appearance, there is stimulation of true differentiation.

BODENSTEIN: Of course, the hormone in sufficient titer freezes, so to speak, all growth.

SCHARRER: All right, but the fact remains that, once the hormone is present in sufficient amount, differentiation occurs, and that, to me, indicates that this type of hormone has something to do with differentiation.

KARLSON: We know that in wound healing, as Wigglesworth pointed out in 1940, there is just the same chain of events, histologically, as in molting, but we have no molt, and we do not know whether the molting hormone is present (in low titer) or not. In this case of cutting up part of the disc, we may have regeneration and a sort of wound healing but not the effect of normal development, which is the concern of this hormone.

SCHNEIDERMAN: Could it be that there is sufficient hormone present to enable this regeneration to take place? In the diapausing pupae of the silkworm you get wound healing without cell division.

BODENSTEIN: I think you are dealing here with regulation, which is something different from regeneration. The building of a new center implies reorganization—regulation of the disc material. Is mitosis present?

HADORN: Yes, certainly. The number of cells of the regulating field parts greatly increase before they begin to differentiate.

SCHARRER: Yes; but still you see two events separated in time; the first is growth, presumably in the absence of a sufficient amount of this particular hormone. The change to differentiation occurs after the prothoracic gland hormone is present.

WILLIAMS: I think that the metamorphosis of the disc is due to the decreasing titer of the corpus allatum hormone. What ensues in metamorphosis is progress in the differentiative act. The decreasing titer of corpus allatum hormone takes the brakes off progress and lets it go ahead.

SCHARRER: Is there evidence that during the last instar there is more corpus allatum hormone in the early stages than later?

WIGGLESWORTH: Yes; in *Calliphora,* if you implant a corpus allatum from the early third stage, you can demonstrate the presence of the juvenile hormone in the last-stage implant, but one does not know about the circulating blood.

SCHARRER: But I am speaking of the titer in the circulating blood.

DAY: Since there are among us some who are not so well up in this field, I wonder if we could decide on one name for each of these hormones.

WILLIAMS: I suggest that we call the hormone from the brain the "brain hormone"; the hormone from the prothoracic glands, the "prothoracic gland hormone"; and the hormone from the corpus allatum, the "corpus allatum hormone."

DAY: It is going to be difficult for some of us to remember to use these names all the time, but I think it will be easier for everybody if we attempt to do this.

WIGGLESWORTH: I wish to join issue with Dr. Scharrer (as I have done in the past) on this question of the differentiation hormone. Now if the word "differentiation" is used in the sense of progress in development, then I agree entirely with her, and I think this is an acceptable term. But if the term "differentiation" is employed in the more usual sense of different cells following different courses in development, I feel then that to speak of a "differentiation" hormone is like speaking of an "individuation hormone," whereas, in fact, the tissues individuate themselves or differentiate themselves by some process which we do not understand. If the term "differentiation hormone" is used in that sense,

I do not think it a permissible term. But it is perfectly clear that this hormone we are speaking about—the prothoracic gland hormone—induces growth (I hope, at a later stage, to have an opportunity to come back and discuss what we mean by that), and that is a prerequisite for this autonomous differentiation.

SCHARRER: Well, I accept all this, but I am not yet convinced that the prothoracic gland hormone is completely neutral with respect to what happens in differentiation.

WIGGLESWORTH: If the hormone controls differentiation, we must suppose that from the small rudiment described by Dr. Hadorn it produces four types of bristles and several organs.

BODENSTEIN: You imply, if I understand you correctly, that the presence of this hormone is a prerequisite for differentiation and that a given cell expresses its inherent differentiation tendencies under the influence of this humoral environment.

WIGGLESWORTH: Exactly, that is my argument. But what does the hormone do?

SCHARRER: It stimulates the expression of potencies for differentiation within the cell. It catalyzes; like any hormone, it does not do something new, it promotes the tendencies inherent in the cell.

BODENSTEIN: It promotes growth at one stage, and perhaps later, at a higher hormone titer, it promotes differentiation.

WIGGLESWORTH: Potential growth is determined by the cell.

GEIGY: I think we could prove what you say with hormone experiments, by taking out the graft ready for differentiation and then putting it again in a young larva. Then you must see that it is not able to be differentiated until the young larva is ready for pupation.

BODENSTEIN: Under these conditions the graft will probably not differentiate. To assure normal differentiation, a sustained hormone action is necessary, at least for a certain time.

SCHARRER: I had meant simply to emphasize that the particular type of experiment that Dr. Hadorn has reported would lend itself to the analysis of this question. That is really all I wanted to say.

RIZKI: Dr. Hadorn, since you have this problem of getting full differentiation of the implant 12–24 hours before metamorphosis is started, can you ligate the larvae at this time, or earlier, and implant into the posterior end to see where the regulation can go further?

HADORN: Yes, it could be done, but we did not do it. Perhaps I should give a definition of what I mean by a "field." If half or any other part of an embryonic area has the capacity to restore all qualities and developmental potencies of the whole area, then we call it a "field."

For instance, if a small part of the original field can form all the bristle types that are normally formed by the entire field, that is a demonstration of such a field organization.

WILLIAMS: I think that the hormonal business is the least interesting aspect of the matter. Here you have a little mass of tissue: you see none of these things in there, and yet, somehow, built into this little mass is a latent organization for all these extraordinary happenings. And you can interfere with this by various reagents and treatments. I wonder if you have any thoughts as to what is the essence of the field. What may be a possible mechanism for the field in the cell?

HADORN: You mean, what it is that makes a part belong to one field and another part belong to another field? Paul Weiss would say different molecular arrangements and populations.

WYATT: Might it be possible to separate these fields and attempt to analyze them by immunological methods, as it is possible that there may be different proteins in them?

HADORN: Yes, one could try it.

WILLIAMS: I was wondering about using treatments and reagents a little more specific than these hypotonic or hypertonic solutions—enzymes, for example. Can you treat the disc and influence what happens?

HADORN: We did not use enzymes. But colchicine acts like a "chemical knife"; it "cuts" the spermatheca field into many parts, each of which will then form a spermatheca. Thus we get up to 12 spermathecae from one single treated field.

POULSON: What happens with regard to rate and pattern of cell division in the so-called "node"?

HADORN: It is difficult to investigate these small cells in the imaginal discs. They are not suited for quantitative work.

### CULTURE OF CELLS FROM INSECT TISSUES

DAY: I know that a number of us are anxious to discuss the subject of insect tissue culture, and this would be an appropriate time to do it. We are all probably agreed that no one has succeeded in culturing insect tissues. Many of the problems that we have been discussing could be attacked if we had adequate tissue cultures. We want to discuss now the reasons for our failure to get repeated subculture and mitoses in culture. If anybody would like to argue that point, I should like to hear it.

WYATT: We had mitoses in some cultures of fibroblast-like cells which migrate out from the larval ovary. I should like to show some slides of these cells in culture. This work, which I think takes us almost to the point where we had continuous culture, was done by my wife. The purpose of it was to obtain cultures for the study of polyhedral virus multiplication; this, of course, had been done by Trager in 1935. The original idea was to repeat his work and see whether it could be adapted for our use. Like Trager, we used explants from the larval ovaries of mature *Bombyx mori* larvae just before pupation. These were explants about 1 mm. in size in hanging-drop preparations with a medium which consisted of salt solution and a small proportion of hemolymph. In an 18-hour culture, interstitial, connective tissue-like cells begin to spread out across the field and fill spaces between the ovarioles. These cells are still reasonably healthy, but they are already beginning to appear rather granular. At 24 hours the cells are degenerating seriously, and little development takes place thereafter, probably more migration than mitosis. These conditions prevail in a medium of Trager's solution with 10 per cent *Bombyx* hemolymph added, and they were clearly unsatisfactory for routine work. So various problems had to be faced. The first was that the hemolymph used had high tyrosinase activity, and this presumably produced toxic substances and was one reason for the degeneration. Eventually we found that they apparently could be removed successfully by heating the hemolymph to 60° C. for 5 minutes, which caused precipitation of about half the proteins, including the tyrosinase. The tyrosinase was not completely inactivated, but it was coagulated, and, if one used the clear supernatant liquid, it would remain indefinitely without darkening.

The next problem was the composition of the medium. In Trager's solution the main salt was sodium chloride, and a large proportion of the osmotic pressure was made up by maltose. The total osmotic pressure gave a freezing-point depression of 0.28° C., which is roughly half that of *Bombyx* hemolymph. His solution did not resemble the composition of hemolymph in any way, but to say this is not to criticize Trager, because at that time little was known about the chemistry of hemolymph, and it was a considerable accomplishment to have gotten a medium which would maintain the tissues as well as it did. When various attempts were made to modify this solution in the hope of improving it—e.g., changing the sugar, changing one or another of the salts, pH, or the osmotic pressure—very little difference resulted, and we eventually came to the conclusion that the solution was so wrong in its ionic balance that changing one or another component had no effect; it was necessary to revise it completely. Some data on the composition of *Bombyx* hemolymph were available to us from the literature. The main cations are, of course, potassium and magnesium. One of the main anions is phosphate, in both organic and inorganic forms. There is a great deal of non-protein nitrogen, partly in amino acids, and a very low value for reducing sugar. We used these data as a basis and then did further quantitative amino acid analyses of our own by quantitative chromatography and made some carbohydrate analyses. The sugars that we found by chromatography were a small amount of glucose and possibly traces of fructose and sucrose, although I am not absolutely certain that these latter were in the hemolymph. But if we did total carbohydrate analysis by the anthrone reaction, we found a large amount of sugar which reacted as glucose but was not glucose. We have recently found that this sugar was trehalose, though we did not know this at the time when we were concerned with tissue culturing. And then we analyzed for phosphorylated derivatives. There was a great amount of organic acid—soluble phosphates and a small amount of inorganic phosphate. So, on the basis of this information, we made up a medium containing amino acids and with the cations roughly in the proportions in which they occur in hemolymph. For the anions we did not have sufficient data, so we used some phosphate and sulfate and made up the balance with chloride. The sugars we put in were those we had found, but in greatly increased quantities, in order to provide a nutrient reserve, as at that time we did not know about trehalose. We put in amino acids in the proportions in which they were found, except that we modified the proportions of glutamic acid, glutamine, aspartic acid, and asparagine, as the hemolymph contained very large amounts of the amides. The organic acids were an empirical mixture made by testing each of these acids in a series of dilutions, finding the highest concentration which caused no inhibitory effect in cultures (i.e., no deleterious effect as determined by the appearance of the cells), and then mixing these. The combination of them did have a definitely stimulatory effect.

This mixture was then used with the addition of about 10 per cent of heat-treated hemolymph. In this medium the cells were very much clearer than before, and they remained in more compact growth. In a 5-day culture the cells were in far better condition than they were at 1 day in the Trager medium. It was possible with this medium to move into roller tubes, in which case small test tubes were used and explants put in 0.15 ml. of medium. In a 5-day roller-tube culture the cells covered the entire glass surface. It was possible to observe many mitoses at this stage, and frequently we could recognize them in metaphase. Mitoses were found after 2 weeks' culture, though they became less frequent.

Now what about hormones and subculturing, and how can we further improve this medium? Most of these questions we were not able to attack, as the work had to be discontinued. We did find in ovaries from mature larvae substantially better development than in ovaries from pupae. In some work with the old medium we found that far more cells were obtained at the beginning or the end of the last larval instar than we obtained at the middle of the instar, and this is also, I think, consistent with the idea that the prothoracic gland hormone may have something to do with it. As for subculturing, we think it should be possible, but these cells are spread thinly as a layer on the glass, and it would be necessary to suspend them, possibly using trypsin. We conclude that insect tissue culture requires a medium that is essentially balanced with respect to the major organic and inorganic nutrients. From that point on, you can add what you want in the way of natural fluids, extracts, and hormones, but, without that, I think that one can hardly hope to get significant results.

DAY: So far as I am aware, these are as good preparations as anybody has obtained. A colleague of mine in Australia, Mr. Tom Grace, has repeated the Wyatts' work and has got similar results. Does anybody know of cultures better than those Dr. Wyatt has shown?

SCHNEIDERMAN: We have taken probably a less sophisticated and less intelligent approach than that of Dr. Wyatt, who actually analyzed insect blood. We have simply tried cultivating insect tissues in various well-known tissue culture media. One medium, which we tried at the suggestion of Dr. W. E. Beckel, of the Canadian Science Service, proved quite successful—i.e., medium T.C. 199 developed in the Connaught Laboratories and commonly used for culturing monkey kidneys for polio vaccine. Having been designed for vertebrates, it would seem at first glance to be as unreasonable a medium as one could think of for insects. But, on the other hand, it contains everything imaginable— amino acids, sugars, purines, and so on. Now the first experiments that Beckel did in our laboratory showed that you could keep the ovaries of the mosquito *Aedes aegypti* alive for 60 days; i.e., they would wave and pulsate. Following this, Mrs. Marcia Loeb and I worked with this medium and improved it somewhat by adding 2 per cent peptone. We began with a tissue which, for students of insect growth, is of special interest—the epidermis. We succeeded in keeping the epidermal cells of diapausing *Cynthia* (*Samia walkeri*) pupae alive for 60 days, as well as many other insect tissues. We employed a variety of criteria to assure us that our tissues were alive. For example, we put a fragment of *Cynthia* heart in a hanging-drop preparation of medium T.C. 199 and then placed an isolated abdominal ganglion on the heart fragment.

Within a few days, at the place where the nerves from the ganglion had been cut, growths appeared which seemed to bind the ganglion to the heart fragment. We then inserted platinum microelectrodes into the hanging drop so that we could stimulate either the heart itself or the ganglion. Two or 3 weeks later we stimulated the heart directly. It required about 6 volts to get it to contract. Stimulating the ganglion with about 0.6 volt was adequate to cause contractions in the heart. Clearly, in this case both the ganglion and the heart tissue were alive, and they remained alive for many weeks. In other cultures Malpighian tubules accumulated neutral red for periods of more than 3 weeks and continued to pulsate in the culture for as long as 6 weeks. Epidermal cells survived the longest of all—2 months—and sent out fibrous processes. I have some pictures here and some camera lucida drawings which you may look at later. Those cells were certainly alive. For example, fragments of pupal leg will pulsate in culture for a long time and will continue to pulsate after several subcultures.

These cells, to be sure, stay alive, but the question naturally arises: Why do they not do something like the cells in vertebrate cultures? Why do they not divide, why do they merely sit? Well, I would not expect them to do anything. These were dormant tissues from a diapausing insect, and in these hanging-drop cultures they do not have a hormonal environment suitable for growth. The fact that they stayed alive for such a long time seems to me encouraging, and it suggests, I think, that one of the biggest defects in insect tissue culture in general is not that the media we use do not contain proper salts, amino acids, sugars, etc., but that they do not contain the proper hormones. I do not suggest that if we add hormones, cultures will grow. Perhaps not, for we must remember that, even with the well-defined vertebrate hormones, only a few have an effect in tissue culture. For example, to get estrogen to have an effect in tissue culture you have to add something as unreasonable as a piece of liver to the culture. The estrogen is possibly in some way attached to protein by the liver and is then able to act. Possibly we may have to add several tissues to our insect tissue culture along with the hormones before we shall get cell division in cultures. However, even though T.C. 199 with 2 per cent peptone will not permit cell division, it is a nice, simple medium which is universally available, and it will keep many insect cells alive for up to 2 months at room temperature. I think that this medium can be useful, even now, to the experimental morphologist. He could, for example, maintain imaginal discs alive for many days and possibly many weeks in vitro.

CASPARI: To keep at least some insect tissues alive for a considerable time, much simpler media may be used. I have observed that hearts of *Cimex* continued to contract for almost a week in hanging-drop cultures of a Beadle-Ephrussi Ringer solution with some added glucose.

WYATT: I should like to mention that we did try medium 199 (we got some directly from Dr. Morgan), and it was completely lethal to the tissues we used.

SCHNEIDERMAN: For spermatocytes it is completely lethal also. The only insect tissue which we have gotten to differentiate in vitro was spermatocytes, which undergo spermatogenesis in insect blood. Unhappily, this is one tissue in the insect that just goes to pieces almost immediately in our artificial medium. Other tissues that are perhaps insulated from the insults of the medium in a more satisfactory way survive for a long time.

WYATT: In some cases bits of heart got into these cultures of ours, and in one experiment, which was done with the old Trager medium, fairly regular visible contractions continued for as long as 6 weeks without any nervous tissue or electric stimulation. So here were cells still alive in this relatively simple medium. It is obviously a very complex problem, and different types of cells have different nutrient requirements. Indeed, Dr. Schneiderman's observation that spermatocytes, the one tissue which will differentiate in culture, degenerate in medium 199 is in line with our feeling that the requirements for development are much more exacting than those for merely keeping diapausing tissues alive. It is worth recalling that diapausing *Cecropia* pupae will withstand all sorts of chemical and physical maltreatment to which the developing insect is sensitive. So I think that merely to demonstrate that one has kept the tissue alive does not necessarily mean that it is going to respond in the normal way to a hormonal environment, and some sort of appropriate balance of major nutrients is probably a prerequisite of your studies.

SCHNEIDERMAN: The only reason that I question the balance of nutrients is that if you take a pupal insect—like a *Polyphemus* pupa—and replace most of its blood with something as unreasonable as distilled water, it will still go on to develop. It seems to me that many insect tissues are singularly resistant to "proper ionic balance." For when you take more than two-thirds of the blood and replace it by distilled water, you are surely doing something very drastic to the ionic balance.

WYATT: The amount of tissue present may be sufficient to replace what you have taken out. It would be interesting to withdraw the "distilled water" again after about 2 weeks and analyze it and see how close it has come to the composition of the blood.

WILLIAMS: There are present about 20 different blood proteins in this insect. When you replace the blood by distilled water, the diapausing animal does not synthesize all 20 proteins. It seems, according to Telfer, to make exclusively one protein. This then builds up quite rapidly in 1 or 2 days, so that the distilled water is made proteinaceous with this material.

SCHNEIDERMAN: In one series of experiments we squeezed out as much blood as possible from the pupa, replaced it with Beadle-Ephrussi Ringer solution, let it sit around for several hours, then squeezed it out again, and replaced it with this same medium. The insect went ahead and developed normally.

SANG: Dr. Schneiderman's reference to *Drosophila* reminds me that no one has mentioned Kuroda's synthetic medium in which he claims successfully to have cultured late wing and eye buds and tumor cells of *Drosophila*. It is true that this medium does not look very impressive as scheduled and that it is much more of an empirical product than Dr. Wyatt's. Also the reports which I have seen provide no real evidence that true growth has taken place beyond what might have occurred in simple saline. But I think this work should be mentioned here and that we should note this claim of successful culture of organs (eye discs with and without parts of the cephalic complex). Organ culture may be a very different matter from the continuous culture of cells, and I think we should recognize this, for it implies two different applications of the tissue culture technique; hormones may be vital to the one but not to the other. Further, Kuroda's success suggests that we can already tackle certain limited problems if we work with organs taken from late larvae which are already well on their way in development.

WIGGLESWORTH: I have got the impression from watching tissues undergoing molting under the effects of hormones that there is something of a hierarchy among the different tissues in their need for hormones for growth and multiplication; and at one end of that hierarchy are the hemocytes. The cells you are describing here I should regard as hemocytes, and they seem to be the ones that can grow and multiply most readily in the absence of hormone, and one might expect that they would be easiest to study in this way.

DAY: Is it agreed that these are, in fact, hemocytes?

WYATT: No, it is not settled. I think they may be hemocytes, for hemocytes do modify their form when cultured in vitro and become difficult to recognize. And, also, hemocytes settle down, and you do not know where you may find them in an insect; but these cells did appear to come from inside the ovarian capsule. The capsule is split open, and you have the ovarioles. I do not know whether there is an accepted name for these cells. Trager called them "interstitial cells." They may be identical with hemocytes and settle down as hemocytes.

HADORN: Did you say they penetrate the ovarian capsules?

WYATT: The cells which grow across the field come from inside the cut ovarian capsule. If we do not cut the capsule, the amount of cell outgrowth is much less.

DAY: Dr. Rizki indicates that he does not believe that they are blood cells.

RIZKI: I think they could be hemocytes, but from a study of the hemocytes in *Drosophila* it looks as though they have a capacity for going in between the cells and encapsulating certain organs. I do not know how, but they become extremely flattened. I shall talk more about that but shall leave it until later, when I shall say something about the normal hemocytes.

WYATT: That interpretation is quite possible.

O'FARRELL: Did I understand that the hypodermal tissues with which Dr. Schneiderman had some success all came from pupal tissue? Did you try larval tissue?

SCHNEIDERMAN: We did not try larval tissue, only pupal tissue and tissue from developing adults. As soon as we put developing tissue into our medium, it spreads out nicely, the same way that the diapausing tissue does, but it ceases its program of development. There is some evidence that the prothoracic gland hormone is necessary not merely as a trigger but as a sustained stimulus for the cells. Thus when you take the differentiating spermatocytes of a *Cecropia* silkworm and remove them from the hormone-containing blood of the developing adult and place them in the blood of a diapausing pupa, which has little prothoracic gland hormone, the viability of these cells is not impaired in the least, but spermatogenesis is brought to a stop. I suggest that this accounts for the cessation of growth in our own cultures of developing tissues. It also probably accounts for the limited growth that you get for a day or two when you place an imaginal disc of *Drosophila* in an artificial medium. People have used the term "momentum" for such limited growth, and I think it is a fair term. The tissues have a certain amount of endogenous hormone, and, when this is used up, growth ceases.

DAY: It seems that insect tissues do not differ from others, in that they can be kept alive for long periods of time. There are two aspects here: one is the medium, and the other is the tissue you are using. Even with all the advances that have been made in vertebrate tissue culture, you still cannot get from the monkey kidney continuous cell growth of the sort which you get in HeLa cells. If this were so, then the Salk vaccine could be made without the continuous importation of monkeys. Not all tissues can be subcultured. There are suggestions that the tissue you use may be much more crucial than we have indicated. I should like to hear some comment on the variation in tissues. Dr. Bodenstein has asked whether anybody has tried embryonic tissues. Mr. Grace has tried every tissue he could lay his hands on, from *Drosophila* eggs before the nuclei have migrated to the periphery and from cockroach embryos at the stage where they can be dissected out of the egg and slit, in the hope that something may grow out from them. Also specimens were used with the hormone system intact, but nothing came out of these either.

BODENSTEIN: There is now a paper out, I think by Jones in England, that shows early action of the prothoracic gland hormone in the embryo.

WIGGLESWORTH: He is dealing merely with what is called "the pre-hatching molt." As you know, these insects undergo a molt or something like a molt which takes place in the egg. It is so like a molt that it is really not very surprising that the hormonal relations are the same as those in later development. The egg has to start developing from a nucleus at some stage.

CASPARI: I wonder whether in this connection it is important to consider that HeLa is a tumor tissue. It has been my impression from the early tissue culture literature that at least some vertebrate tumors are excellent material for tissue culture under non-optimal conditions. I should like to know whether anybody has made attempts to culture some of the well-known *Drosophila* tumors.

SCHNEIDERMAN: As far as maintenance is concerned, insect cells like the epidermis will live as long in T.C. 199 as will vertebrate cells that do not divide. As Morgan, Morton, and Parker have shown, the survival period is about 2 months. Perhaps the 2 per cent peptone should do something to it, but it does not. We have also maintained a pupal silkworm brain in this medium for 2 months, taken the brain out, put it into a diapausing pupa without a brain, chilled this pupa, and then this pupa initiated development. So it seems that the secretory capacity of the brain's neurosecretory cells was not impaired by a prolonged period in this medium.

If you want an organ, say the brain, to live in vitro, you disconnect it from all its connectives, take it out, and then put it back into the animal. Let it remain in the animal for a couple of weeks, where it can get used to "living alone." Under these conditions it heals up nicely, and then you can remove it and culture it. This seems to me to be a much better way than to culture the freshly excised organs, which possibly release toxic products and so on. You get the insect to heal up the organ you want to study and then you remove it.

Factors like oxygen tension must also be considered in insect tissue culture. When you remove an organ like the brain, make sure that the two large tracheal tubes are intact and contain bubbles of air. These bubbles persist for weeks in the culture; that is, the brain has two little lungs into which oxygen can diffuse from the medium and into the tissue. This kind of procedure makes it easier to keep organs alive.

KARLSON: Have you done this with a ball of epidermis like the preparation of Piepho?

SCHNEIDERMAN: No, we have not.

DAY: What we want are suggestions for things we might try which will make these tissues undergo continued mitoses. It is suggested that we put in the right pinch of magic stuff, probably a hormone or a balance of hormones, and then insect tissues will go ahead. But this is not true in vertebrate tissues. Either you do not need this material, or if you do put in hormones, they do not have, as Dr. Schneiderman has said, very much effect. Now is this a fundamental difference between insect tissues and vertebrate tissues—that they must have this hormone? Embryo extracts, as Dr. Wigglesworth suggests, have been tried, and they are without any effect whatsoever.

HADORN: If you take out of the vertebrate body important hormone-producing glands, like pituitary and thyroid, it still grows, and it differentiates to a certain extent. Can you do a corresponding experiment in insects?

SCHARRER: I do not think it has been done in insects.

HADORN: Well, without any pituitary you get very good differentiation.

KARLSON: I think it might be that the insect is much more dependent upon hormones than is the vertebrate.

SCHNEIDERMAN: There are several people here who have studied isolated abdomens of various insects. They do not have endocrine organs, so far as we know. They just sit there and do nothing. I think that in the medium T.C. 199 insect tissues behave as they do in isolated abdomens. And, indeed, they should be doing nothing, for they have no prothoracic gland hormone.

CASPARI: It appears to me, from what has been said, that too close a comparison of insect and vertebrate hormones may be misleading.

There may be some differences in the general functions of these hormones in the two groups of animals. All known insect hormones control developmental processes; more specifically, they affect the direction of the differentiation of cells. Among vertebrate hormones, only the sex hormones determine differentiation processes, the others are involved in the control of more or less generalized metabolic processes, such as basal metabolism, ion concentration, glycogen storage. It should be added that some of the vertebrate hormones—insulin and the hormone of the parathyroid—are necessary for the survival of the individual. Other glands, such as the pituitary and the thyroid, can be removed without killing the animal.

BODENSTEIN: The only time that tissue culture has really worked in differentiation is in spermatogenesis. If you take larval blood and put the spermatogonia into this blood, you do not get anything. You place them in pupal blood, and you get differentiation of spermatozoa. Now, if you take larval blood and add purified hormone, what happens—do they "go," or do they "not go"?

WILLIAMS: No, they do not do anything. The hormone that promotes the growth of the spermatocytes and differentiates the growth of the sperm is non-dialyzable and heat-labile and so on. If the growth factor in this medium is the prothoracic gland hormone, it is bound to a protein. I think the ecdysone may get itself bound to a protein in the intact animal before becoming active. Evidently, there is an active conjugation that the insect does somewhere in the body. But it does not happen spontaneously if you add ecdysone to blood in the test tube.

WYATT: What happens if you inject ecdysone into a stage that does not normally contain active hormone and then, after a suitable period, withdraw the hemolymph? Is it then active?

WILLIAMS: I get the impression that that works. The experiment is not clear because, obviously, you have to inject ecdysone into an isolated abdomen; otherwise you do not know whether the hormone you get out is coming from the prothoracic gland in that preparation. You must do it in the isolated abdomen. The trouble is that the isolated abdomen has experienced a lot of surgery. There is a lot of toxic stuff in the blood, and this blood is not a good culture medium.

KARLSON: I should like to make two remarks—one is on isolated abdomens which do not produce the hormone, of course, and seem to do nothing. In our experience they do more than nothing; that is, they reverse the potencies of reacting to hormones. If we hold isolated abdomens for 2 or 3 days, we get a lesser response to a hormone injection than if we take them after the first day of ligation. This is true in *Cal-*

*liphora* as well as *Ephestia*. We concluded that the reactivity of the tissue goes down; and the isolated tissues (in culture) would go down, too, in 3 or 4 days. And the second point is on spermatocytes. A specific growth factor for spermatocytes, that is, a gonadotropic hormone or something of that sort which is formed soon after development begins, could explain the results of certain experiments. This has to be tested and can be tested if we take active blood and follow the same procedure that we normally do when extracting ecdysone. You must (if you have a combination of protein and ecdysone) get active extracts from this blood. If you have only some sort of gonadotropic extract, then you should get nothing, but, of course, you must have the purified protein as a compound.

WILLIAMS: Of course, everything else in the animal reacts at the same time as the spermatocytes. So you could predict without doing any experiments that the hormone is present in this active blood. This does not decide on the larger question you raise as to whether the factor promoting spermatocyte differentiation is a gonadotropic hormone. I think this is the prothoracic gland hormone itself. This is an economical assumption. There is nothing that argues that it is not the same hormone.

KARLSON: Yes, but it is not yet proved.

SCHNEIDERMAN: One point to clarify this: at those periods when the prothoracic gland hormone is present, that is, before the larva molts to a pupa and the pupa to an adult, the spermatocytes will develop in the blood. If there is a gonadotropin present, then it must be secreted whenever the prothoracic gland hormone is secreted, i.e., during the pupal-adult transformation and at pupation.

WILLIAMS: During the larval molts, the prothoracic gland hormone is also secreted, but the corpus allatum hormone is present, and consequently the spermatocytes do not differentiate. You can say that if this is a gonadotropic hormone, it follows like a shadow behind the prothoracic gland hormone.

SCHARRER: What do you mean by "gonadotropin active in the larva"?

SCHNEIDERMAN: I did not introduce the term!

SCHARRER: I think Dr. Karlson means prothoracic gland hormone?

KARLSON: I would only like to say a hormone specifically necessary for the growth of spermatocytes.

SCHARRER: Yes, but you have to specify it. If it is active in the larva, it would, according to all we know, come from the prothoracic gland and not from the corpus allatum. There is a difference.

KARLSON: Yes, but there is the possibility of still another source of internal secretion whose activities are not yet known.

SCHARRER: Well, I do not think we have to postulate such an additional hormone source.

DAY: I do not think we are going to get very much help from the hormone story until we know more about what to add and how to add it. Is this the general opinion?

WIGGLESWORTH: There is another important factor, which is, of course, the co-operation of the tissues. What you have is a testis alone and a blood medium, but what you may want are the other tissues, the pericardial cell system, the many varieties of hemocytes, the fat body, and there may be many other tissues that we do not know of that may be co-operating.

SCHNEIDERMAN: The kind of experiment Dr. Wigglesworth suggests is to take various tissues and to make mixed cultures, take Malpighian tubules to excrete, add a piece of fat body, a fragment of heart to stir the medium around, etc.

DAY: This is extremely discouraging when what we want is a layer of cells like one we get in HeLa cell cultures. Is this going to be possible?

WYATT: Just a minute! The layer of cells similar to HeLa cells I think we can already get. I think a continuation of our type of work will provide that, but this is not going to give the answer to the question of differentiating tissues.

DAY: Well, the difference between your cells and HeLa cells is that the HeLa cells can be continuously subcultured.

WYATT: I suspect that doing that for ourselves is a purely technical problem of finding the right medium and the mechanical question of how to suspend the cells and transfer them from one tube to another.

BODENSTEIN: You realize that in vertebrate tissue culture one usually deals with growing, and not differentiating, tissues. Now it seems to me that you have already succeeded to some extent in growing, in culture, a fibroblast-like cell type of insect tissue. If you could subculture these cells, you would have a real insect tissue culture method.

RIZKI: Referring to the idea of Dr. Hadorn's of active and reactive system, we should concentrate on the site where this hormone acts—the morphological site. In plants, auxin acts on the cell wall. Now is it possible that the insect hormone or hormones result in changing the permeability of the cell? We ought to try some substances which change the permeability of the cells to see what would be the result.

WIGGLESWORTH: That is the burden of a communication I would like to make at a later stage—perhaps in connection with the diapause problem.

### DIFFERENTIATION OF SPERMATOCYTES

WILLIAMS: I propose to show several lantern slides based on the work of the late Edmond Schmidt on the differentiation of spermatocytes, which may be of technical importance in this whole problem. Schmidt cultured spermatocytes from diapausing pupae. Spermatocytes are in thousands of little balls of epithelioid cells. As Wigglesworth suggests, this is one of those tissues that are easy to culture—the only insect tissue so far, I think, that has behaved in vitro in substantially the same way as in vivo. So you can take these little balls of cells and put them in a hanging-drop culture in a depression slide. Now, if you use as a medium the blood of the diapausing pupa—blood that lacks prothoracic gland hormone—the cells live a very long time but never develop. However, if you use blood that contains prothoracic gland hormone—that is, blood that you get from an animal during the first days of adult development or from a caterpillar approaching pupation—then, within a few days, you see an astonishing series of things happen. First, there is a cleavage of these epithelioid cells by mitotic divisions. Then you get the two meiotic divisions. And now each of these cells grows a long tail, and the whole cyst begins to elongate. This occurs in 3–7 days in the hanging drop containing hormone. The whole thing is elongated now. The cysts of spermatocytes turn themselves into a great elongate bundle of spermatozoa. This happens, as Schmidt has shown, only when you use as a culture medium what we call "active blood." This is blood containing the prothoracic gland hormone but lacking the corpus allatum hormone. The factor that promotes this reaction is non-volatile. It is heat-labile, and I think it is the prothoracic gland hormone—ecdysone conjugated in some way to a protein. This, then, is the career of these little balls of cells in culture. They do exactly the same thing at the outset of adult development if you leave them in the animal. They react to the same endocrine milieu as do all the other tissues in the pupa at that time.

Now my present purpose is to call attention to a very peculiar thing that was shown in the course of Schmidt's work. If you use a hanging drop under a depression slide, it is absolutely crucial that the culture be tightly sealed. If the cover slip is placed the least bit ajar, then, instead of the growth and differentiation of these cells, their death follows rather promptly.

This was a complete mystery for several years. Only lately with Melvin Ketchel have we come back to this problem. Why must the system be tightly sealed off from the environment? To make a long story short, it turns out that this is not, as you might suppose, the generation in a closed space of some critical low concentration of oxygen or critical high concentration of carbon dioxide. If you use a much larger culture chamber sealed tightly and containing hormone, a single culture in the middle of the large chamber behaves as if the chamber were not sealed tight. We found that we had to place, not one culture in there, but at least eight. When you place eight cultures in a chamber of this larger volume, they undergo a normal growth reaction.

The explanation of the phenomenon seems to be as follows. When the cells react with hormone, there is produced within the medium a transformation of some non-volatile precursor into an active growth factor which is volatile. This substance then partitions between the fluid medium and the gas phase. If the gas phase is infinite (as it is in a system that is in continuity with air), then the loss of the volatile factor brings the reaction to a standstill. And now, instead of causing the growth reaction, the hormone actually promotes the death of the cells. We were able by various maneuvers to show some of the solubility characteristics of this factor. It can be adsorbed on activated charcoal and dissolved in certain lipids. It is quite soluble in insect blood. It is substantially insoluble in aqueous or polar solvents. My objective in introducing the matter is to suggest that there is produced in the course of the hormonal growth reaction—that is, generated by the interaction of the cells and hormone—a catalytically active substance which is formed from a non-volatile precursor that pre-exists in the blood medium. Both the cells and the hormone are necessary for the production of the factor. The volatile factor is then necessary, in addition to the hormone, for growth and developmental reaction.

Thus far we have been able to test only the spermatocyte system. But again it is an economical assumption to suppose that the growth and differentiating reaction of these cells is a good model of what is going on in other cells. This suggests that the reaction involving the non-volatile precursor's changing to a volatile factor is perhaps a generalized thing. Perhaps one must minimize the gas phase in insect tissue cultures or in some way promote the accumulation of a critical titer of the volatile factor in the medium. It is reasonable to suppose that, in the developing animal, the volatile factor is continuously lost from the animal via the tracheal system and, in a steady-state manner, is replaced from the non-volatile precursor. At the present time we are trying to find out what this volatile factor is. It is, of course, reminiscent of the ethylene situation in plants; the reaction of ripening of fruit by auxin causes the generation of ethylene, which is then necessary for the reaction to proceed. The volatile factor in the insect is evidently a small molecule of distinctive solubility. One should be able to collect it by freezing the gas stream in liquid air and then, by vapor-phase chromatography, to find out what it is.

DAY: I have always been afraid that there would be found a volatile hormone. It is particularly unfortunate from the point of view of what we want to do with it.

WILLIAMS: The volatile factor is not the hormone, nor can it substitute for the hormone. The hormone is necessary in addition to the factor.

KARLSON: I should like to make two remarks. The first is that it is hard to understand that the cells do not undergo development in the change in the larva to the pupa. It might be that, up until that time, the precursor is not formed, so that the volatile factor cannot be produced. And the other point is merely a vague idea—whether this volatile factor can be related in some way to the sex attractant of the female moth, which, we know, is also volatile. I will not suggest that it is the same thing, but perhaps somewhat related.

WYATT: Do you have direct evidence that it is produced as a result of the interaction of the cells and the hormone? Is it possible that this is something which cells produce anyway as part of their normal metabolism?

WILLIAMS: I do not think so. In the testes you cannot get it produced unless you have cells and hormone present. You can do this by adding donor drops within the chamber and recipient drops and so on. As Ketchel and I described a year or so ago, it can be shown that these ingredients are all necessary for the production of the stuff.

SCHNEIDERMAN: If you surround one drop with hormone with, say, eight drops without hormone, you will not get that to grow?

WILLIAMS: No. You must have all components together in the same drop in order to make the stuff. Then the stuff can partition out into other drops in the chamber. Consequently, in a large chamber, such as I have shown on the slide, you need eight or more hanging drops of standard volume so that the partition to the gas phase will still leave in the drops a sufficient concentration.

WIGGLESWORTH: I think this is an extraordinarily interesting bit of work. It really throws an entirely new factor into the whole field, and I am rather sorry to degrade the discussion into a mere matter of terminology. But there *is* a matter of terminology which I think is of importance. I notice that in these remarks, as has been done before, this process is described as "differentiation." Now if that progressive development of these spermatocytes into spermatozoa is differentiation, then I am entirely in agreement that this hormone from the prothoracic gland is a differentiating hormone. But we are here using "differentiation" in two quite different senses. When Dr. Hadorn talked this morning about differentiation in his discs, he was using it in the other sense. I have thought a good deal about this, and I think that this is a real basis of disagreement.

DAY: Have you got another word to describe the situation in the spermatocytes?

WIGGLESWORTH: No, I am afraid I call it "differentiation"!

RIZKI: The important aspect of this is the rearrangement of the cytoplasmic elements in a single cell, and what Dr. Wigglesworth is implying is differentiation at a tissue level, and in that sense it is a very different thing.

BODENSTEIN: I do not see this. What is the difference between the differentiation of a single cell into a sperm and the differentiation of one or two cells into a bristle?

WIGGLESWORTH: That is quite right. At the cytological level it is the same thing, but I would again consider that it is the cell which is looking after its own differentiation, provided that it has the adequate environment, which involves this hormone and the volatile factor and so on.

HADORN: If you use Waddington's epigenetic landscape, this may be differentiation. That is what happens when you are already in a valley.

WADDINGTON: I am not quite sure what the point at issue is here. "Differentiation" is a word that is conventionally used in two different ways. First, it means the continuation of a certain course of developmental change, which may be done by a single cell in developing into a bristle, or in the development of a spermatid into a sperm, or by a group of cells forming the brain of an insect. In all these cases, there is a continuing of one and the same course of developmental change, and differentiation is a change in *time*. In a second sense, it means that a large area of tissue which was originally homogeneous breaks up into different parts and becomes heterogeneous—and that is differentiation in *space*. In my recent book I suggested that this second type is actually much better called "regionalization," and in Germany it is often called "arealization." There are several other meanings of "differentiation," but those are the major ones—the change in *time* and the change in *space*.

BODENSTEIN: But, of course, arealization goes on in time too. It takes time before the different phases take place.

WADDINGTON: Yes, but the essential point of regionalization is that the various geographical regions become different from one another. In the other meaning of "differentiation" the geographical region changes its character without splitting up.

DAY: Dr. Williams' contribution was, I think, very appropriate to the subject we were discussing earlier on tissue culture, and I should like to hear whether anybody has any ideas on how it may be put into effect in the cultures. I do not think the answer is simply to use small culture chambers.

WILLIAMS: I think that you have to supply this volatile stuff to a large gas phase, or economize on the gas phase, or generate this stuff in some way within the system. I think, also, that, in addition to the kind of setup suggested here, if you want sustained growth as in mammalian tissue culture, you must somehow oppose the acting-out of the careers of the cells to a terminal state. Obviously, you get a lot of growth, mitoses, and reduction divisions—and then you end up with spermatozoa, which is a terminal state. This culture then grows no more. In order to get the sustained kind of culture that people want for a study of insect viruses, one has to oppose this progress which the prothoracic gland hormone favors. The only way that the insect opposes this progress is to have present the corpus allatum hormone. And I should think that the corpus allatum hormone would be a good thing to have in the medium if you want cultures to continue to grow. Now that that hormone is available, I should think that it would be a good idea to add some to these cultures.

CARLSON: I wonder if the situation you describe might not be a special case existing in tissues that in the normal state have rather impermeable protecting envelopes. In tissues such as the grasshopper or *Drosophila* embryo, where the outer covering of the egg is very thin and probably more permeable to gases and fluids than in a pupa, cultured tissues might be less affected by the volume of inclosed air in the culture.

WILLIAMS: I do not think that that is so, because each of these little cysts is a cluster of epithelioid cells which have a very thin layer of surrounding epithelium—so thin that it is almost like the intima of a blood vessel. It is true that, with special techniques, you can see this surrounding cellular layer. But I do not think that it protects the spermatocytes very much. What does protect these cells in the intact animal are the various envelopes of the testes. We, of course, remove such membranes in our procedure and liberate the spermatocytes from the testes.

CARLSON: I was thinking of the capacity of the outer covering of the whole pupa, or the puparium, to retain volatile materials.

WILLIAMS: Every cell of an insect has its lung in the form of a tracheole of some sort, and I cannot see any way of preventing the loss of the factor from the tracheal system.

DAY: A suggestion has been made that the studies which Dr. Wyatt has carried out so beautifully may have less application to tissue culture than we have supposed, because most of the tissues are invested by a connective tissue sheath, of the permeability characteristics of which we are completely ignorant. It may be that the medium in which these tissues are bathed is not the medium surrounding the cells. Has anybody any views on that?

WILLIAMS: I am sure that what you say is so—at least in most insects. I do not think that insect blood is the intercellular fluid of insects. No one knows what it is.

WYATT: It is certainly true that hemolymph itself is a very unsatisfactory medium for the type of cells that we were growing, even when tyrosinase had been removed. So it seems paradoxical that we were attempting to imitate hemolymph, but perhaps the undesirable components may be enzymes which were not included in the synthetic mixture. Then, again, it may be true that the cells we were getting were, in fact, hemocytes, or closely related to hemocytes, and then this medium is nearer the correct one.

WADDINGTON: One question of a technical nature: We know that if we put an imaginal bud of *Drosophila* into the body of an adult, it goes ahead and develops and also if you put it into the body of a larva. Now what happens if you put a bud between the hypodermis of the pupa and the pupal chitin? There is quite a lot of fluid there, as you know, after the pupa has contracted away from its pupal skin—about its properties I know nothing. But is it known whether imaginal buds do actually develop in this space, which is actually external to the body of the fly?

WILLIAMS: Yes, I have done that. If the implant survives, you find that it has been sucked back in and comes to lie just below the hypodermis. If it stays in the molting fluid, it dies. One has to think where one can look for this intercellular fluid. I do not think anybody has ever had any. But I suspect that one might find it in the cavity of the testes or in some place like that. I tried to encourage Dr. Ramsay of Cambridge to go ahead and examine the composition of this fluid.

It should be fairly easy to get intercellular fluid. I predict that it will have no close resemblance to insect hemolymph.

DAY: As in all questions we cannot answer, we can go on discussing tissue cultures for a very long time. Has anyone any further ideas which he thinks might assist in the solution of the problem?

CARLSON: In regard to your comments on permeability, we have been quite interested in getting the grasshopper embryos we use in neuroblast studies to live longer than they do and to undergo mitoses longer. We have tried quite a few different methods, using the whole embryo and using its yolk, just squeezing it out of the yolk on the cover glass and making a hanging-drop preparation with various mixtures of the yolk with physiological salt solution, but we have never had much success. I have wondered sometimes whether the relationships between the yolk and the membranes through which it has to pass to get to the embryo may be important and whether we may destroy some of them in the process of making the preparation. There is fluid under the membrane that covers the ventral surface of the embryo, and then there is the outer mass of yolk material that becomes disarranged and broken in making the preparation.

SCHNEIDERMAN: Dr. Carlson, you have succeeded in dissociating the cells of insects by enzymatic means; how long do those dissociated cells survive?

CARLSON: I have not done this myself. M. E. Gaulden, G. S. St. Amand and S. R. Tipton, K. Dan, and H. S. Roberts have isolated grasshopper neuroblasts by adding trypsin and hyaluronidase to calcium-free medium and breaking up the embryonic tissues mechanically. Roberts watched individual cells proceed through three complete cycles of division and reported one case in which there were apparently normal divisions going on 11 days after the preparation had been made.

GEIGY: I want to draw your attention to one possibility of application of the method to keep arthropod tissues alive for a longer period, not in the field of metamorphosis but for the field of epidemiology and bacteriology. We have been studying in Basel in the Tropical Institute the behavior of spirochetes in the body of the tick, transmitting these spirochetes which cause relapsing fever. We can state already that spirochetes penetrating the mid-gut come into the general cavity and there are attracted by the organs of the tick, mainly by the ganglion, by the ovary, by the coxal organs, and by the salivary glands. But they are not attracted by the muscles, by the Malpighian tubes, by the fat body, and so on. So there is a certain polarity for these spirochetes, and we are now studying in tissue culture the relative attractiveness of different tissues. We do not need to maintain these tissues for a very long period; ten days will be enough, because the attractant is very strong and the spirochetes penetrate very quickly and are attracted very quickly to the special organs. We hope to study not only the specificity of these organs in connection with the spirochetes but also to introduce special substances in very fine capillary tubes, in order to determine what substances are attractive to pathogenic agents. We have not been very successful in maintaining the tissues for a long time. We get up to 9 days only, especially for the ovary of ticks, and the difficulty in our case is that we cannot very easily change the medium because the medium is at the same time a suspension of spirochetes. So we have to make all the observations in about 9 days, to keep the spirochetes alive and the tissues alive. Up to now we have seen that spirochetes are strongly attracted by ovaries, a little bit less by brain, and about in the same manner by the coxal organs of adult ticks, and strongly by the salivary glands of young tick nymphs, and this is absolutely the same as in the live tick. I only want to show you that this can be a very important method to study all kinds of pathogenic agents, besides the problem of development, and I think we shall develop these methods with Schneiderman's and other methods and adapt them to this other problem. The chamber in which we keep the tissues and spirochetes must be very flat because we have to observe the spirochetes under the dark field for 8 or 9 days as they progress from one part of the chamber to another, where the tissue is waiting to be inoculated by the agents.

TRACHEAL PATTERNS IN THE REGENERATED LEGS OF COCKROACHES

DAY: There are certainly a lot of applications for insect tissue culture, and a lot of people are working on it in many parts of the world, and I am sure we shall succeed before too long. Now Dr. O'Farrell has some material which he would like to present on tracheal patterns, which has implications for development but relates particularly to what he will say tomorrow on regeneration.

O'FARRELL: It did occur to us, working on the regenerating leg of *Blattella,* that we ought to look into the way in which the tracheae invaded a blastema, which begins as a mass of cells that show no regionalization (to use Dr. Waddington's phrase), and we found in unstained whole-mount preparations, injected by the Wigglesworth cobalt sulfide technique, that immediately after the removal of a leg the main coxal trachea comes right down and almost touches the blood clot. Now we have found that there are two small tracheal branches which nor-

75

mally seem to supply the hypodermis of the trochanter and that these branches alone are responsible for the tracheation of the blastema. In a preparation made 2 or 3 days after leg removal, the main trachea has retracted with the rest of the contents of the old coxa, and one of these minor branches is now becoming very conspicuous. At a later stage some muscles and the elements of the main joints of the leg are already recognizable. The subsidiary branches are now moving around and pulling the main trachea into a hook or loop. The original backwardly directed tracheal supply going back into the coxal musculature is present too; and one can see two lines which are the tracheae of the regenerate. This pattern persists, and when the regenerate is externalized at the molt, it has an entirely new, effective tracheal supply derived from these secondary branches. One can see quite clearly the stump of the old main trachea and the new tracheation provided from the secondary source. Exactly the same thing occurs whether one performs the operation before the critical period of the instar, in which case one gets a complete regenerate at the next molt, or after the critical period, in which case one gets a papilla at the next molt and a regenerate at the succeeding molt. The modified pattern, once established, seems to work all right and undergoes no further modification. If you look at the tracheal system in one of these regenerates several molts later on, it still shows the same basic origin, and there is no sign of re-establishment of the original type of supply. The regenerated leg can thus be recognized by its tracheal supply, as well as by the absence of one segment in the tarsus. In regeneration there is apparently no question of a solid mass of cells growing out into the regenerate and becoming air-filled only at or near the molt. The tracheae supplying the blastema are injectable and hence air-filled long before the molt. So there is a possibility that the provision of this highly modified direct supply to the regenerate may be essential for proper muscle differentiation, which seems to follow on the arrival of the tracheae in the femur/tibia region of the blastema. Also, of course, this utilization of a supply which has normally nothing to do with the distal part of the leg is not merely temporary but becomes definitive and permanent in the completed regenerate. This may be of some interest in relation to the question of tracheal patterns which is on the agenda.

# · IV ·

## Metamorphosis and Diapause

---

### EYE-DISC TRANSPLANTATIONS IN WILD AND MUTANT FLY LARVAE

POULSON (*presiding*) called for Dr. Bodenstein's remarks and also announced Dr. Geigy's film on "Feeding Mechanism in *Rhodnius*," to follow the session.

BODENSTEIN: I shall show the results obtained after grafting eye discs among different genera of Diptera. These experiments involved two separate problems: an analysis of eye-color development and tissue compatibility.

We have in our laboratory two eye-color mutants, one *Musca domestica* and the other *Phormia regina*. The eye color of both mutants is a yellowish green, strikingly different from the missing reddish-brown pigment. The question now arises, Is the biochemical system underlying the expression of the brown-eyed pigment in both these Diptera similar to that observed and analyzed in *Drosophila* by Beadle, Tatum, and Ephrussi, and in *Ephestia* by Kühn and his school? To this end, transplantation and injection experiments were performed.

When the eye disc from a wild *Musca* donor is transplanted into a green *Musca* host (all transplantations to be discussed were performed on late last-instar larvae), the implant develops into an imaginal eye of wild-type pigmentation. The graft thus develops autonomously. However, it changes the green color of the host eyes toward pink. The graft has released into the blood of the host a diffusible substance or substances necessary for pigment formation in the host eye. The reciprocal experiment, namely, the transplantation of a mutant eye disc into a wild-type host, corroborates the first experiment. In this latter combination the mutant green implants give rise to a pigmented imaginal eye almost indistinguishable from a wild-type eye. The wild-type host must have contained an appreciable amount of a diffusible principle on which the mutant eye depends for pigment development. Now the diffusible principle responsible for these effects is produced not only by the eye but also by other wild-type tissues. A color change in the eyes of the green host can be brought about by the transplantation of ovaries and Malpighian tubes from wild-type donors, while the transplantation of antenna, leg, and halter discs, as well as testis, has no effect. The diffusible principle is also not genera-specific, for eye discs of *Phormia, Callitroga, Sarcophaga,* and *Cynomia* transplanted into the green *Musca* mutant change the whole host eye color toward wild type. Not only the eye pigment of the *Musca* mutant but also the pigmentation of the testis sheath depend on this diffusible principle, for it was found that whenever a wild-type tissue graft changed the eye color of the mutant host, it also elicited pigment formation in the sheath of the testis—which in this mutant is colorless but is yellowish-brown in the wild-type fly.

The story of the green-eyed *Phormia* mutant is a slightly different one. If eye discs taken from the *Phormia* mutant are transplanted into wild *Musca* hosts, they develop in their new environment to imaginal completion and give rise to eyes with almost normal wild-type pigmentation. Thus, like the mutant *Musca* eye discs, the mutant *Phormia* eye discs respond to diffusible substances circulating in the blood of wild-type *Musca* flies. However, the substance responsible for the pigmentation of the two mutant eyes must be different in nature, because, when the eye discs of a green *Phormia* mutant are transplanted into hosts of the *Musca* mutant type, both transplant and host eyes become pigmented. The transplant apparently supplies the diffusible principle necessary for the development of pigment in the host eye, and this in turn produces the factors needed for pigment formation in the grafted eye.

The resemblance between these results and those obtained in other insects, notably *Drosophila* and *Ephestia,* in which it has been shown that the diffusible principles were intermediate compounds of tryptophane metabolism, made it obvious that we should try the effect of these substances also on our material. Consequently, pure preparations of kynurenine and 3-hydroxykynurenine were injected into the two green-eyed mutants. At this point I must depart for a moment from the discussion in order to thank Dr. Karlson for his kindness in making available to me the 3-hydroxykynurenine preparation used for these experiments. Now to continue with the narrative. It was found that injection of kynurenine into the *Musca* mutant changed its eye color toward wild, while the eye color of the *Phormia* mutant remained green, i.e., did not change after kynurenine injection. Quite different was the course of events when the metabolite 3-hydroxykynurenine was injected. This compound changed the eye color of both the *Musca* and the *Phormia* mutant toward wild type. The evidence thus suggests that the biosynthetic chain leading to the formation of the wild eye pigment is interrupted at different points in these two mutants. The *Musca* mutant is unable to convert tryptophane into kynurenine, while the *Phormia* mutant is unable to transform kynurenine into 3-hydroxy-kynurenine. Thus the biochemical system underlying the expression of the brown eye pigment in both these Diptera is much the same as that found in other insect forms.

We have also made a preliminary study on an eye-color mutant of the American roach, *Periplaneta americana*. This mutant has yellowish-white eyes, while the normal roach eye is a dark brown. The lack of eye pigment in the mutant roach is apparently not caused by the absence of diffusible substances in the blood. When the wild and mutant animal are combined in parabiosis, the eyes of the mutant partner remain colorless, although perfect blood connection between these partners was established and the pairs lived for several weeks. It is possible that the genetic constitution of this mutant has disturbed in some way the proteinaceous carrier granules to which the final pigment granules are bound. But this aspect of the problem needs further investigation.

Finally, a few words concerning the question of tissue compatibility. I believe it is interesting that intergeneric eye grafts can be made successfully among a rather wide range of Diptera. Thus eye discs of *Phormia, Callitroga, Cynomia, Fucellia,* and *Sarcophaga* develop to imaginal completion when grafted into *Musca* hosts. The same is true for *Musca* eye discs transplanted into *Callitroga* and *Sarcophaga*. While the eye tissues proper differentiate to imaginal completion in all the combinations named, part of the hypodermis of the head (which is always included in the graft) and its specialized components, such as hairs, bristles, etc., fail to develop from *Callitroga* and *Phormia* grafts in *Musca* hosts. In such cases one observes in the histological picture large degenerated areas next to the well-differentiated eye tissue components. When larval ovaries of *Phormia* are transplanted into *Musca* larvae, the transplants seem to become incompatible only after metamorphosis—a situation familiar to the amphibian embryologist. These ovarian grafts develop in synchrony with their hosts until the latter emerge from the pupa, but further development ceases from this stage on. No egg maturation occurs, not even the beginnings of yolk deposition. Such ovaries do not degenerate, but they remain immature. I think the most striking result from the developmental point of view is that transplants among such different genera are compatible and that in certain combinations certain tissues of the same type differentiate while others do not. This is something we ought to look into.

79

HADORN: Is anything known of the intergeneric transplantation where only certain organs develop? In Amphibia you get the incompatibility reaction only after metamorphosis. Different tissues exhibit different degrees of incompatibility; i.e., some tissues are first affected by the incompatibility reaction, others only later, and some not at all.

WADDINGTON: This appears to be an immunological reaction, similar to that with mammalian or avian skin.

SCHNEIDERMAN: But insects do not produce antibodies in the ordinary sense. How widely has this interordinal and interfamilial graft transplantation been carried? I know Dr. Wigglesworth has done experiments on interordinal transplantation of corpora allata from *Calliphora* to *Rhodnius*.

BODENSTEIN: Often even closely related species may be incompatible. For instance, *Drosophila virilis* tissue develops well in *melanogaster*, whereas *melanogaster* does not develop in *virilis*.

SCHNEIDERMAN: If antibody reactions are not responsible for this incompatibility, what kinds of reactions are, in fact, responsible?

SCHARRER: Was there not old work by Huff which indicated the existence of these reactions?

SCHNEIDERMAN: I know many people have tried carefully with modern techniques to demonstrate the production of antibodies, but with very little result.

WYATT: There is plenty of work by Chorine and Metalnikoff and other earlier workers which indicates some form of acquired immunity to bacterial infection, but the more recent work with purified proteins has not given any reaction, so far as I know.

CASPARI: Dr. Bernheimer and I have attempted to immunize the caterpillars of several saturniid species against a number of antigens, including red blood cells, bacteriophage, and a protein toxin, streptolysin O. We did not find any evidence for the formation of circulating antibodies. Furthermore, in cases where apparent reactions occurred, it could be shown that they differed from vertebrate antibodies in specificity, sensitivity, and stability and, in short, were something different altogether. This, of course, raises doubt about those cases in the literature in which circulating antibodies in insects have been reported.

It seems unwise, however, to generalize from these observations that insects do not form antibodies. Even in mammals and birds, the young do not form antibodies, and Bernheimer has just obtained results which show that frog tadpoles do not form antibodies, whereas metamorphosed frogs do. Since caterpillars are larval forms, it seems to be wise to wait until experiments on other stages of insects, including adults, have been performed.

WILLIAMS: Pappenheimer and I, some years ago, using the most sensitive test system known—the diphtheria toxoid system—tried to establish the production of circulating antibodies to toxoid. We found it quite impossible to make any circulating antibodies. However, this does not negate the prospect of having tissue-bound antibody reactions of the tuberculin type. Perhaps the antibodies are univalent and are bound in tissues. The question I have is whether those white-eyed flies were blind.

BODENSTEIN: They are not blind, and they are not white, but green-ish yellow. The green is apparently a granular pigment. Both mutants look very much alike and presumably have the same kind of pigment.

WADDINGTON: I wanted to draw attention to two points concerning intertissue reactions during development in *Drosophila*. They are both rather different from what we have had before in *Drosophila*. One concerns the development of the dorsal flight muscles. It started from the observations that in Bithorax the extra mesothorax does not contain flight muscles, and we asked the question, Why does it not have muscles? Dr. Shatoury in our laboratory studied this and went into the general question of how the dorsal flight muscles develop. The dorsal flight muscles are built up on the basis of three larval muscles, and the first contributions of imaginal tissue are mesoderm cells coming from the mesothoracic bud. A few hours after puparium formation, you get cells from the mesothoracic bud around the larval cells. Then they penetrate into the larval muscles. Nothing much further happens until about 30 hours after puparium formation, when you see, in a transverse section, the beginning of the trochanteral depressor of the second leg, corresponding to the mesothorax. Cellular strands from this are connected up to the region of the larval substratum of the dorsal flight muscles, and it is when this connection is made that the three larval muscles are broken up, each into two, giving a set of six muscle rudiments from which the dorsal flight muscles then develop. That looked as though the contribution from the trochanteral depressors was doing something to the dorsal muscles. And if you remove a second leg bud in a late larva just before pupation, you find that you do, in fact, suppress the formation of the flight muscles. In such an animal you find that, on the side from which the second leg bud is removed, the dorsal flight muscles are almost gone. You have only the remnants of three larval muscles which should form the substratum, and not only the longitudinal flight muscles but also the lateral set of muscles are missing. Muscles of the second leg bud have, therefore, got to migrate up and join with the mesothoracic mesoderm, which is accumulating around the larval muscles, and it is the combination of the two which develops the dorsal muscles. It is the only example of an inductive reaction in the classical sense which I know of in *Drosophila* development. In Bithorax, by taking out one of the mesothoracic buds, the metathoracic buds can be persuaded to move forward above the second leg thoracic bud, and you can have muscles induced in it, if you are lucky. But that is a complication.

The other story is another example of a tissue interaction. It was done in quite a different way by Dr. Pantelouris of our laboratory. This is rather parallel to the work that Ebert has been doing in the chick, demonstrating the presence of tissue- or organ-specific substances. By growing *Drosophila* larvae for a short time on radioactive methianine, you get the various organs labeled by radioactive sulfur, and you can transplant a given organ into an unlabeled host. There is evidence that the label tends to go reasonably specifically into the corresponding organ of the host. In the case where you have a good eye graft, showing a count of 25, you get 12 in the host eyes as opposed to 1.5 in the brain, etc.; there is a little more in the gonads but still not as much as in the host eye. Of course, the brain and muscles are doing an enormous amount of protein synthesis, and you cannot explain the high uptake in the host eyes on the basis that it is only the eyes that are doing the synthesis at that time. Moreover, if, instead of eyes, you graft ovaries, you again have the label going mainly to the corresponding organ. The figures are lower, but you have more going into the host ovary than into the muscle or brain. This is a preliminary indication that these organs are producing organ-specific substances which can pass around in the body. Whether these substances do anything important we do not know. Dr. Weiss, as you know, has quite elaborate theories of their effect in growth control and so on. I do not want to comment on this at the moment but just say that in *Drosophila* there is at least evidence that such substances do exist. They are counted from sections. In a thing like the ovary, we do not count limited areas but the whole of it. It is so heterogeneous that you get high and low counts in different regions, and the only way is to count the whole area and then measure the area. In brain, which is relatively homogeneous, we count a number of areas of known size. In the eye, we again count the whole thing.

WILLIAMS: There is a possibility here that I mentioned to Waddington in Edinburgh; i.e., if muscle anlagen are denervated in any way by the experimental procedure, then they should never develop. Nüsch, in

Basel, has studied that. It is clear that the genesis of the muscle in the course of metamorphosis requires not only hormones but also something that is delivered directly to the muscle anlagen by nerves. It seems that this is the only tissue within the animal that needs something so delivered. Nüsch has been able to trace the innervation of all these anlagen in silkworm pupae by systematically cutting the nerves and seeing which muscles fail to form in the adult. Once formed, the preservation of the muscles does not require innervation. But the actual formation of the muscles does require innervation.

WADDINGTON: I do not know the result of cutting the nerves to the dorsal region. If the metathoracic bud of a Bithorax shifts forward and joins up with the mesothoracic elements, it may then develop muscles; this strongly suggests that there is an inductive action. But I agree that the sectioning of nerves has to be looked into.

RIZKI: I was thinking that it would be very interesting to implant a specific leg disc along with the unlabeled disc complex and then see whether the labeled disc still contributes to the corresponding implanted unlabeled disc.

WADDINGTON: Yes, it would be interesting to do that, but these results are very preliminary. I think the insects are particularly interesting because of the possibility that there are specific first-leg, second-leg, and third-leg substances, for example.

### EFFECTS OF ECDYSONE

POULSON: The major part of this afternoon's discussion was to be on "arrested development," and I should like to ask Dr. Karlson for his remarks about this.

KARLSON: I am concerned with hormones and not so much on arrested growth as on the setting-in of growth and molting after a period of rest. We tried injections of the prothoracic gland hormone, ecdysone, in different species. In all experiments we used pure crystalline ecdysone, with the exception of the second one, in which we used purified extracts containing approximately 5 per cent of the hormone.

The ordinary *Calliphora* assay is very sensitive. A dose of 0.0075 $\mu$g. of crystalline ecdysone per animal produces about 70 per cent puparium formation; that is what we call "one Calliphora unit." The pupation of the ligated larval abdomen of *Galleria* (this species reacting somewhat better than *Ephestia*) needs a much higher dose; we have followed the histological changes which are the same as in *Cerura*. About this later. Professor Williams tested the activity of the hormone in diapausing saturniids. Brainless pupae as well as isolated abdomens will

**83**

develop after the injection of ecdysone; and you have molting in the decapitated *Rhodnius,* which Professor Wigglesworth will talk about in detail.

We did some more work on the color change in *Cerura vinula* which may be of interest. The next experiments deal with the effects of ligation. They were done by Dr. Buckmann in Mainz. The last-instar caterpillar is normally green with a dark-red design on the back, but it changes its color a certain time before pupation. That the color change can be stopped by ligation suggests that a hormone is responsible. I should mention that the color change occurs about $6\frac{1}{2}$ days earlier than pupation, and the histological changes in the epidermis (mitosis, thickening of the epithelium) are not yet set in motion. We tried to reproduce the color change in ligated abdomens by injection of ecdysone; this is possible with a rather small dose, approximately 50 Calliphora units. The pigments involved are of a type I have already discussed. Xanthommatine is present and its derivatives dihydroxanthommatine and rhodommatine. The reduced pigments are bright red, the oxidized form is dark red or brown. The reduction apparently occurs after the pigment is formed, so that we have here a natural redox indicator built into the epidermis; this tells us what the enzymatic environment may be. In normal development, after the first deposition of pigment in the epidermis, more pigment is formed in the fat body, then in the mid-gut, and, finally, shortly before pupation, the pigment in the epidermis is metabolized so that the caterpillar becomes green again.

On injection of a higher dose, you can suppress the deposition of pigment in the epidermis, the fat body becoming stained immediately. If you give a much higher dose, you arrive at an atypical pupal molt, without any preceding color change. A dose of 3,000 Calliphora units is needed to get the atypical molt in which a thin cuticle is laid down, the epidermis undergoing the typical changes described by Kühn and Piepho in 1938. The histological changes are the same as in *Ephestia*. Moreover, a diapausing abdomen of *Cecropia* can also be transformed into a completely normal imaginal abdomen by injection of approximately 10 $\mu$g. of ecdysone.

WIGGLESWORTH: I should like to make one comment on those figures of mine of 0.5- and 0.75-$\mu$g. dosage. I should point out that those injections were made on insects decapitated 24 hours after feeding. Such insects never molt without added hormone. But they have, as I have since come to realize, already secreted substantial amounts of prothoracic gland hormone, so that the real dose would be substantially greater than that, and I would suggest that you mentioned the same phenomenon this morning when you referred to your *Calliphora* larvae, that if you waited some time, you required a larger dose of ecdysone. You said that the reactivity of the tissues had fallen; I would say that ecdysone already present in the tissues had been utilized.

KARLSON: It might be true that it is metabolized, that if you ligate, wait, and inject somewhat later, some is used up, and you may have to add this to the crucial amount in order to get the reaction. And it might be that, in order to get the color change in *Cerura*, in which you get a clear-cut effect with a very small dose, you need a higher dose to produce the next event. This reflects the fact that ecdysone is present 6 days before pupal molt and is acting on the tissue; and it is only in this favorable object that you can see anything about its action.

POULSON then called on Dr. Wigglesworth to present his data.

WIGGLESWORTH: I should like to point out that *Rhodnius* feeds just once in each molting stage and that is all that is needed for each molt, and the meal is followed by secretion of the hormone. When that molt comes to an end, the tissues become dormant, and no signs of growth can be seen. Now at that stage there may still be plenty of undigested blood in the stomach, so that this is not a question of nutrition; and it was these observations, of course, which led to the suggestion that in the arrest of growth, or diapause, in other insects the immediate cause might be the failure of these growth-producing hormones, an idea that has been well substantiated by the work of Williams and others. Now we have just seen from Dr. Karlson's slides that the injection of ecdysone will interrupt this diapause and restart the growth processes. Dr. Karlson very kindly supplied me with some of his precious hormone, and that has greatly facilitated the study of its mode of action. I did some work in conjunction with Dr. Karl Zwicky of Dr. Hadorn's department on the consumption of oxygen during the molting cycle in *Rhodnius*. In the unfed insect the oxygen consumption is at a very low level. Very soon after feeding, the oxygen consumption increases; it rises steadily for 5 or 6 days and then remains at a high level, often showing a peak at the time of molting; it then falls during the next 5 or 6 days, down to a new low level. A corresponding peak occurs at the next molt, followed by a fall, so that from one molt to the next the oxygen consumption follows a U-shaped course. I suggest that that is the nature of the U-shaped curve in the pupal stage of other insects. Now what is the meaning of this curve? We interpret it as essentially a curve of protein synthesis. Of course, there are other syntheses in progress, but by far the most important is protein synthesis. After feeding, you get a rapid buildup of cytoplasm in the epidermis, you get ribonucleoproteins being formed within a few hours after the injection of the hormone or after feeding; you first get the increase in cytoplasm, then mitosis occurs, and you get multiplication of cells. By this stage, even by the first day, these cells are already adding to the existing cuticle. Then you get the period of mitosis, which is not reflected in this curve at all. By the time of molting, only about two-thirds of the cuticle has been formed, and during 5 or 6 days after molting the remaining one-third of that cuticle is added.

Another problem we have been working on is the cycle of growth in the sternal muscles of the abdomen. These muscles are very important for the act of molting, but soon after molting the muscles disintegrate; soon after feeding, protein synthesis is restored, the new fibrils are laid down, and that process continues right up to about the day before molting. A first-stage larva, newly hatched from the egg, shows perfectly formed little muscles; then 3 days later they have broken down—and that happens in every molt.

What we wanted to observe were the changes in the cells when exposed to ecdysone. I have taken three kinds of cells as examples. In fat-body cells of the newly fed larvae are small nucleoli, and the mitochondria are mainly coccoid in form. A day after feeding or injection of ecdysone the nucleoli are enlarged and the mitochondria transformed to filamentous forms. Thus a terrific amount of active metabolism must be going on in these cells.

The second tissue, which is more interesting, is the epidermis in the arrested condition from a fourth-stage larva, showing small nucleoli. After injection with 1 $\mu$g. of ecdysone in Ringer solution, the nucleoli become enlarged and the mitochondria swollen. You get some of these changes within 6 hours. An electron-microscope section of epidermis shows mitochondria with an average diameter of 0.15 $\mu$; 6 hours after the injection of ecdysone, the mitochondria are swollen and have an average diameter of 0.28 $\mu$. The trouble with the electron micrographs is that one can see so few cells; the light microscope shows the same thing in thousands of cells.

The third tissue is muscle in the resting stage. There are no fibrils, and the nucleoli and mitochondria are small. A day after feeding, the mitochondria are greatly enlarged and often lie in longitudinal rows between the fibrils, which are just beginning to crystallize out. We interpret these results as indicating that the hormone is restarting protein synthesis. Now, according to current ideas on protein synthesis, the oxidative phosphorylation cycle in the mitochondria is providing energy, probably in the form of ATP, which is funneled into a specific enzyme system, perhaps located in the ribonucleoprotein-containing microsomes, which then links the amino acids together in the appropriate order to produce the specific proteins. There are many points at which breaks might occur in this chain, arresting this synthetic process. Williams has suggested that the break occurs in the oxidative phosphorylation stage with the elimination of cytochrome c. The hypothesis that I am putting forward is that, in fact, we have the whole enzyme system here but that in the dormant stage the enzymes are in some way segregated from their substrates and the hormone is loosening things up and increasing intracellular permeability and facilitating access between these enzymes and their substrate. Now that is a pretty non-specific stimulus, similar in effect to that produced by injury to the epidermis of the adult *Rhodnius*, which normally is permanently in the dormant stage. A day after a very small incision is made in the epidermis you get exactly the same changes in the adjacent cells as from the hormone. This I would roughly describe as an effect of products of autolysis from the wound spreading through the tissues and producing perhaps something like a mild cytolysis, facilitating contact between synthetic enzymes and their substrates.

SCHNEIDERMAN: Is it possible that injury is simply lowering the threshold of these cells to the hormone that is normally present?

WIGGLESWORTH: Yes, very small amounts of hormone may perhaps be circulating in an adult some weeks after molting. But it has no thoracic glands.

WYATT: Are there mitoses in the epidermis after injury? I take it that this is one of the early results of the hormone.

WIGGLESWORTH: Mitosis is a rather late result of the hormone. These changes I have been describing occur in the first 24 hours. Mitosis usually does not begin until about 4 days. In the case of injury, of course, you do get mitosis. You get cells activated and migrating inward and then you get mitosis in the periphery where the activated cells are sparse.

WADDINGTON: In protein synthesis are not the most striking changes in the nucleoli? In many embryonic tissues the radioactive amino acids are picked up first in the nucleoli, and these seem to be playing a major part in protein synthesis. It seems that one of the most striking results of ecdysone is the enlargement of the nucleolus.

WIGGLESWORTH: I quite agree; it is generally accepted that protein synthesis is associated with an enlargement of the nucleolus, and this is strikingly shown during fibril formation in the muscles. According to current ideas, the nucleoli are connected with production of the ribonucleoprotein in the cytoplasm.

WADDINGTON: I thought current ideas tended to emphasize the microsomes rather than the nucleoli.

WIGGLESWORTH: I thought they had rather come together. The nucleoli are conceived of as producing either ribonucleoproteins or histones, which are themselves templates for ribonucleoproteins. All I am doing is quoting current ideas.

HADORN: In the resting stage of muscle have you really only nuclei, membranes, and mitochondria?

WIGGLESWORTH: But no fibrils. You must take my word for it, the longitudinal folds in the membrane look like fibrils. It is not easy to distinguish them.

BODENSTEIN: What do these muscles do? How long are they real muscles?

WIGGLESWORTH: They are building up during the period of about 10 days before molting; then, when the insect molts, they are active for only a few hours, and then they are demobilized within 3–4 days. They are used for producing blood pressure to blow out the limbs, etc.

HADORN: It would be interesting to find out quantitatively about the free amino acids present in these muscles and whether synthesis of proteins occurs only from free amino acids or from bigger complexes.

WIGGLESWORTH: The blood is full of free amino acids, and they are presumably raw materials.

O'FARRELL: What happens to the attachments of these muscles?

WIGGLESWORTH: The birefringement component in the fibrils disappears. It ends rather short of the insertion, but it all disappears during this process of breakdown.

KARLSON: I should like to refer to Dr. Schneiderman's suggestion that the threshold of the tissue to the hormone is lowered. From extracts of *Bombyx* we obtained 1,800,000 Calliphora units from pupae and only 160,000 units from the same amount of moths. These moths were 1 day old, and probably the hormone titer will go down in the next few days of life.

HADORN: Are you certain that your method of titration gets all the stuff out?

KARLSON: That is what I mean by "rough approximation." I cannot claim to have achieved a quantitative determination of the hormone. In experiments showing differences of 1 to 10, the relation may be 1 to 8, but they are, at least, true differences.

BODENSTEIN: Another question about lowering the threshold of the cells: In your animals, Dr. Schneiderman, do you get cell division only at times of molting?

SCHNEIDERMAN: That is correct. You can give a *Cecropia* pupa an extensive injury, and it will heal, but it does this by spreading itself thin, and no mitosis occurs. But the changes that occur in the cells after injury are similar to those that occur in an animal about to molt, e.g., increased basophilia, etc.

BODENSTEIN: In *Periplaneta* the cells behave exactly the same. They migrate to the site of injury and thin out around it. During the next molt, the thinned-out regions fill up again, so that equilibrium is established. But after bigger injuries cell division occurs before molting. So the extent of the injury is important.

SCHNEIDERMAN: We have inflicted maximum injury on our pupae by removing half their cuticle. If you repeat this injury, the insect will finally run out of stuff. After a half-dozen wounds the epidermis ceases to spread, but the blood cells still come around for about 12 wounds. But, finally, even they cease coming to the wound site. But we never get mitosis in the epidermis, even after the most extensive injury.

BODENSTEIN: Is there a possibility that, when the cell density is reduced, the cells become more sensitive to the hormone?

WILLIAMS: Two years ago, Donald Fawcett made for us thin-section preparations of the wing epithelium of diapausing pupae. He commented that these were the most empty-looking cells that he had ever seen. They had a scant population of typical mitochondria, but there was practically no trace of endoplasmic reticulum. When the hormone comes in, one apparently gets a new generation of mitochondria plus endoplasmic reticulum. So this would be largely in agreement with what Wigglesworth has said.

WIGGLESWORTH: When a cell is making cuticle, it becomes solid with this laminated type of endoplasmic reticulum and basophilic cytoplasm. I did not show electron micrographs of it, but we have them.

WILLIAMS: Another point which bears on this protein synthesis: Telfer, at the University of Pennsylvania, has studied the kinetics of radioactive amino acid incorporation into the proteins of the blood during diapause and during development. Development is accompanied by a fourfold increase in the kinetics of incorporation into protein. A curious thing is that injury also causes a fourfold increase. And, even so, no development occurs after injury if the animal is brainless. So, notwithstanding the fact that the brain is absent and notwithstanding the fact that the animal is in permanent diapause, injury speeds up the protein turnover fourfold.

WIGGLESWORTH: I imagine that is largely being effected by hemocytes.

KARLSON: I would return once more to the question of mitosis. The color change in *Cerura* is simultaneous with the mitotic period in the wing anlagen; mitosis in the epidermis occurs only about 7 days later. Both are induced by the same hormone. This would mean that the cells of the imaginal disc have a lower threshold to the hormone. The same might be true for other cells.

O'FARRELL: My impression from watching regeneration in *Blattella* is that hypodermal cells tend to undergo mitosis when they have room to do so, whether from being stretched apart or otherwise, and this may be a factor in lowering the threshold to the hormone.

WIGGLESWORTH: So far as mitosis is concerned, the distance between neighboring nuclei is a very important factor. We found years ago in *Rhodnius* that if you induce the unfed insect to molt by parabiosis to a molting insect, you can get molting and everything else with virtually no mitosis, since the nuclei are so close together already that they do not need any new ones. You get exactly the same thing in these wounds. You get mitosis, not up against the wound, where the effect of the stimuli is strongest, but at the periphery, where the cells are sparse.

HADORN: This is a very general effect which is found in vertebrates as well as in insects. Two stimuli are required: first, one for migration, induced by the wound, and, second, one for mitosis, which starts where the cell concentration becomes thin.

SCHNEIDERMAN: There seems to be an antagonism between the processes of an insect healing its wounds and the initiation of development. If you wound a *Cecropia* pupa repeatedly and get it to heal many times, you can delay for a long time the initiation of development. When you wound an animal, its respiration increases tremendously, and this respiration is cytochrome oxidase–mediated, like that of the developing adult. This gives one the idea that either the animal can have this wound respiration and engage in wound healing or else it can have other kinds of developmental events and morphogenesis. It cannot do both. I ask my question particularly because I know Dr. Wigglesworth has alternative views.

WIGGLESWORTH: And I should like to reply to it! One must not forget the hemocytes. If you inject foreign matter into the insect or implant a piece of celloidin, growth is delayed, and that delay seems to be correlated with the activity of the hemocytes. These are engaged in phagocytizing foreign materials or surrounding implanted celloidin, and, when that happens, growth is delayed, but why I do not know. Perhaps the hemocytes are producing some protein necessary for the proper formation of the prothoracic gland hormone. It may be that they are actively removing the brain factor from the blood. But the interference with the hemocytes is important, and I believe that the effects of injury on growth may be related to these effects on the hemocytes.

BODENSTEIN: Is it possible that the hemocytes do something which stops the gland from secreting?

WIGGLESWORTH: That is another possibility.

BLOOD CELLS OF *Drosophila* AS RELATED TO METAMORPHOSIS

POULSON: We are coming to a discussion of the mode of action of hormones. There are a number of pieces of evidence which seem to bear on this.

RIZKI: I have been studying the blood cells of *D. melanogaster,* and some of the phenomena I have observed are related to metamorphosis. My observations are based on the Ore-R wild strain and two strains which develop melanotic tumors or pseudo-tumors. I have studied the hemocytes prepared by several methods: in vitro examination of hemolymph samples with the phase microscope, stained blood smears, and slides of sectioned stained specimens. Throughout the larval life there are two classes of hemocytes (Fig. 6). The cells of one type are spherical, with more or less smooth cytoplasmic contents, and I have called them the "plasmatocytes." The cells of the other type are large and spherical, with numerous crystalline cytoplasmic inclusions. These are the crystal cells. Approximately 95 per cent of the hemocyte population throughout larval life consists of plasmatocytes, and the remainder are crystal cells. As the time of pupation approaches, a sudden change in the blood cells becomes apparent. The plasmatocytes now have many fine filaments, or pseudopods, extending from the cell surface, and I have called these transformed plasmatocytes the "podocyte variants." This is the first step in a morphological transformation of the plasmatocytes. This phenomenon of cellular transformation continues until eventually the cells become extremely flattened and disclike. I have called these flattened cells "lamellocytes." It would seem that there are certain factors in the hemolymph at pupation time, perhaps the hormones, which act upon the cells.

I have examined the blood of two tumorous strains, and alterations in the blood cells of these strains are apparent prior to the appearance of the melanotic masses. The plasmatocytes undergo a precocious transformation, and these transforming podocytes and lamellocytes then aggregate around other tissues in the body. In one strain, tu$^w$, aggrega-

91

tion occurs around the posterior fat body, and in another strain, mt$^A$, masses of hemocytes accumulate. These cellular accumulations then become melanized. It is interesting that the first changes begin to appear in the blood of the tu$^w$ tumorous strain around the time of the second molt.

When a hemolymph sample is examined with the phase microscope as quickly as possible after removal from the body, the crystals can be seen intact within the crystal cells. After 5 or 10 minutes some of

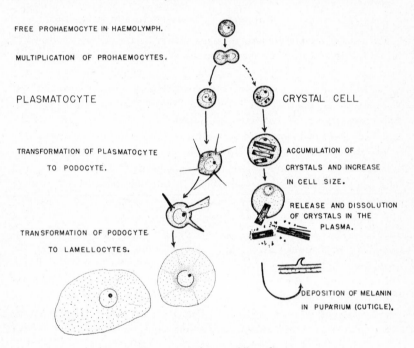

FREE PROHAEMOCYTE IN HAEMOLYMPH.

MULTIPLICATION OF PROHAEMOCYTES.

PLASMATOCYTE

CRYSTAL CELL

TRANSFORMATION OF PLASMATOCYTE
TO PODOCYTE.

ACCUMULATION OF
CRYSTALS AND INCREASE
IN CELL SIZE.

RELEASE AND DISSOLUTION
OF CRYSTALS IN THE
PLASMA.

TRANSFORMATION OF PODOCYTE
TO LAMELLOCYTES.

DEPOSITION OF MELANIN
IN PUPARIUM (CUTICLE).

FIG. 6.—Hemocytes of *Drosophila melanogaster*

the crystal cells begin to swell and burst, and the crystals are released into the hemolymph. Within a few seconds they completely dissolve in the hemolymph, and a vesicle containing a nucleus is all that remains of the crystal cell. Some of the crystal cells appear to swell but do not burst; in this case the crystals can be observed to disappear in the cytoplasm. The type of experimental treatment determines the site of pigmentation, and this site is correlated with the condition of the crystal cells. If the crystal cells remain intact, blackening is restricted to these cells; if the treatment ruptures them, diffuse pigmentation will be found outside these cells. These observations are based on examination of larvae. I have not studied this problem any further as yet, but it would be interesting to follow the fate of the crystal cells in relation to pigmentation of the puparium.

GEIGY: How can you be sure about this cycle of plasmatocytes? Are you sure that the cycle goes this way and not another?

RIZKI: When you take a sample of hemolymph just before the white puparium is formed and examine the cells in a hemolymph suspension, the plasmatocytes are nice round cells. But if you take the sample of hemolymph and make a smear, you do not get these round cells but ones in which the edges are all jagged. There are some points from the surface of the cells from which these fine filaments, or pseudopods, are thrown out. I have a long table of data of the frequency of the differential counts of these cells throughout larval life, and the changes exactly correspond: when the plasmatocytes decrease in frequency, there is a corresponding increase in the podocyte variant. When the white puparium is formed, the podocyte frequency shoots up, and, after this, lamellocytes appear only at the end of the process. When the brown puparium is formed, the blood cells are much harder to study, because other tissues are beginning to degenerate, and remnants are extracted with the hemolymph.

GEIGY: Where are all the plasmatocytes coming from for podocyte formation?

RIZKI: The cytokinetic index is so high (up to 13 per cent) that it is sufficient to account for the increase in the hemocyte population throughout the larval life by mitotic division. I do not know really what is the content or nature of these flat cells, the lamellocytes. It is possible that they form barriers around the organs of the larvae which are in the process of metamorphosis. This is a very interesting problem. It looks like an adaptive type of change, since in the tumorous strains very specific tissues are associated with the transformed cells.

GEIGY: In the metamorphosis of Diptera I could never understand why all at once there are hundreds of these cells. And then in regard to these names—"podocyte," "lamellocyte," etc. Did you create these names by yourself or have others used them before?

RIZKI: I have simplified the classification of J. F. Yeager, which was extremely complicated. Most of the blood cell classifications are very complicated, but here we have a much simplified situation; I think Cameron had worked out the same kind of simplified classification. Arnold has been working on *Ephestia*, and this classification can be applied to his results. Now we have good evidence that cells do change during larval life. The term "podocyte" has been used by previous workers, but I do not know of any previous description of the lamel-locyte transformation.

HADORN: Do you not believe that new blood cells are released from the blood-forming organs?

RIZKI: I have not seen any critical evidence that this occurs. The only time that I have seen disintegration of the blood-forming organs was in the brown pupa when some of the posterior cells from the blood-forming organs became loose. The observations are not sufficient, but they are certainly in line with those made by Robertson. I have not worked on this aspect of the problem, and I believe it is one which requires further study.

### DIAPAUSE IN EMBRYOS OF *Melanoplus*

BUCKLIN: We have studied diapause in embryos of the grasshopper, *Melanoplus differentialis,* and, as a background for the presentation of these results, I shall briefly remind you of the main features of the development of this embryo. A disc-shaped germ band forms on the yolk surface at one end of the egg. This germ band elongates, a tail-like process extending along the yolk surface until it reaches approximately the mid-point of the egg. The elongate germ band then develops indications of the boundaries between head, thorax, and abdomen, completes segmentation, develops limbs, and, by the twentieth day of the 38-day embryonic period, consists of an embryo "lying on its back" on the yolk surface, its head at one end of the egg, well enough developed to be recognizably "grasshopper-like," but its dorsal surface incomplete and open to the yolk.

At this point the embryo goes into diapause. Progress in gross morphogenesis ceases, cell division stops, and the respiration drops to a low and cyanide-insensitive level.

When diapause is terminated by chilling or other treatments, the respiration increases and becomes cyanide-sensitive, cell division recommences within 1 day, and in a few days the embryo undergoes blastokinesis, a striking revolution of the embryo around the yolk mass, reversing its position in the egg. During and after blastokinesis the dorsal body wall is completed by growth around the yolk, and the embryo increases in length until all the yolk is inclosed in the gut and the embryo extends from one end of the egg to the other. The embryo then molts, completes its differentiation, and hatches.

Diapause can be terminated experimentally in whole eggs by chilling, by immersion in xylol, and by other treatments. We have recently discovered that diapause can also be terminated by removing the embryo from the eggshell and "explanting" it to hanging drops of Ringer solution. The diapausing embryo can be easily removed from the shell by cutting off one end of the egg and squeezing out the embryo lying on the surface of the yolk, the whole inclosed by the cellular serosal membrane. The serosa is usually ruptured by this procedure but heals within a few hours.

Such an explantation immediately terminates the diapause. Mitotic activity is resumed, and within a few days the embryo goes through the movements of blastokinesis. In most of the embryos, development then proceeds at the normal rate to the stage of hatching. In fact, some of these embryos have been removed from the hanging drop, dried off, and raised through the first nymphal instar.

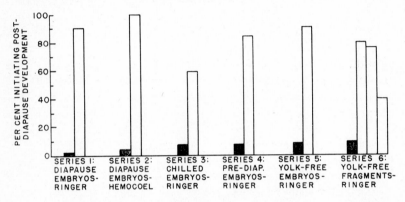

FIG. 7.—Initiation of postdiapause development in explanted embryos. *White bars,* experimentals; *black bars,* controls. Further explanation in text.

This phenomenon of termination of diapause by explantation has been studied in several media with several different types of embryos, as shown in Figure 7. I shall not give the full data but simply sketch the results, which will be published in detail elsewhere.

Most of the experimental series shown in Figure 7 were set up as follows. The contents of one pod of eggs, approximately one hundred eggs, were divided into two parts. About fifty of the embryos were explanted into hanging drops, and the remainder were kept in the shell on filter paper as controls. Each of the bars in the graph represents at least fifty embryos. A few of the diapausing controls resumed development "spontaneously," but this was always less than 10 per cent and always represents a significant difference from the experimental embryos.

In the first series of experiments, diapausing embryos were explanted to hanging drops of Ringer solution. More than 90 per cent of such explanted embryos initiated postdiapause development, as indicated by the completion of blastokinesis. Less than 2 per cent of the *in ovo* controls showed blastokinesis.

In the second series, diapausing embryos were explanted to the hemocoele of adult grasshoppers without their yolk and serosa. Two days later, the embryos were removed from the hemocoele and sectioned, to permit observation of mitotic activity. All the embryos showed mitotic activity at a fairly normal rate, indicating that diapause had been terminated by explantation under these conditions.

In the third series, chilled embryos were explanted and also showed blastokinesis, as would be expected, since the diapause had been terminated by chilling. The percentage blastokinesis in chilled explants is somewhat lower than in unchilled diapausing explants, presumably because of the fact that the serosa tends to break down, and blastokinesis can, therefore, not be successfully achieved.

In the next series, embryos were removed from the egg 16 days after laying, that is, 4 days before the time at which they would normally enter diapause. These embryos went through blastokinesis 6 days after explantation at precisely the time at which they would normally have undergone blastokinesis if they had omitted the diapause. Apparently, diapause can be prevented, as well as terminated, by the explantation treatment.

In the fifth series, embryos were removed from the egg, divested of yolk and membranes, and then placed in the hanging drop. The experiment was done to test the suggestion that the effective cause of diapause resides in the yolk system (the yolk plus the vitellophage cells). It has been postulated that, at the beginning of diapause, the vitellophages cease their normal activity of transferring nutrients from the yolk to the cells of the embryo. The inception of postdiapause development would then be due to a reactivation of the yolk system, which recommences transfer of necessary nutrient materials to the embryo. This theory does not fit with the results of this series, in which the yolk-free embryos also commence postdiapause development. They cannot undergo blastokinesis, since they lack yolk and serosa, but a high percentage show the inception of mitotic activity that is characteristic of the commencement of postdiapause development. Cell division continues for a few days at approximately the same rate as in a normal embryo with yolk, after which time the rate of cell division decreases and the embryo finally dies, presumably because of exhaustion of stored nutrients.

We were surprised to find that such yolk-free embryos maintained mitotic activity for 2 or 3 days, even though explanted to a non-nutrient medium. The cells were thought to be practically devoid of stored food material and dependent on a continuous supply from the yolk system. However, Miss Kaocharern in our laboratories has recently demonstrated, in fresh preparation, large amounts of lipid material in diapausing cells, stored as small droplets. This stored food apparently represents the energy source for the long-continued growth in explanted fragments, and its presence is another indication that the block in diapause is not in the yolk system but within the embryo proper—an inability of the embryonic cells to metabolize nutrients which are continuously available.

In the sixth series, yolk-free fragments of embryos were explanted. The embryos were removed from the egg, completely freed of yolk and membranes, and cut into four pieces: abdomen, head and thorax together, and two separate metathoracic limbs. The pieces were explanted to separate drops. All types of fragments initiated postdiapause development, as indicated by the inception of mitotic activity. Approximately 70 per cent of the anterior and posterior halves and approximately 50 per cent of the isolated limbs showed cell division, although at less than the normal rate. The experiment indicates that the explantation causes initiation of postdiapause development by acting directly on individual embryonic tissues—cells not only removed from the yolk but also isolated from influences of the brain and other known endocrine structures.

We then modified the explant medium to determine whether some specific component of the Ringer solution was stimulating the diapausing cells to recommence growth and differentiation. Whole diapausing embryos, with yolk and serosa, were explanted to isosmotic solutions of each of the salt components of the Ringer solution. Blastokinesis occurred in isosmotic sodium chloride but not in potassium chloride or calcium chloride. Isosmotic solutions of the non-electrolytes sucrose and mannitol did not induce blastokinesis, but explantation to mannitol did induce a low rate of cell division, accompanied by severe pyknosis. Thus the precise ionic composition of the explant medium seems immaterial to the effect of explantation in inducing development.

Nor is development seriously affected by changes in the concentration of the Ringer solution. Embryos explanted to twice-concentrated Ringer showed blastokinesis with a frequency only slightly lower than in normal Ringer. Half-concentrated Ringer was even slightly more effective in inducing development than was Ringer of normal concentration. So the embryo can recommence development in a rather surprisingly wide range of salt concentrations.

In summary, the results presented so far indicate that explantation by these methods brings about the termination of diapause by exerting a direct effect on the individual cells of the embryo, without participation by localized endocrine centers and without mediation by the yolk system. Moreover, the inception of postdiapause development occurs in media of widely varying composition and concentration. Such results seem to support a theory presented by Slifer, that the cessation and resumption of development in this embryo are caused by the cessation and resumption of the uptake of water into the egg. The effect of explantation could be explained economically by saying that explantation simply provides the diapausing cells with free access to water. This is at the moment a working hypothesis and is, of course, not the only possible explanation.

In order to uncover possible further clues as to the precise manner of stimulation of development by explantation, we have turned our attention to the events which occur within the embryo shortly after explantation. The first study was directed to determining how rapidly mitotic activity resumes after explantation of a non-dividing embryo. Tahmisian some years ago showed that mitotic activity is resumed in previously chilled whole eggs within about 12 hours after return to 25° C., and we have found that a similar situation obtains in explanted embryos. In one typical series, mitotic figures were counted in Feulgen smears of embryos fixed every 24 hours for 4 days after explantation. At 24 hours, about five hundred figures were found in each embryo; and in the next few days the count rose rapidly to several thousand figures per embryo. The variation is considerable. To increase the number of figures and thus facilitate counting, we added colchicine to the Ringer solution in which embryos were cultured and found at 24 hours more than four thousand c-mitoses per embryo. A high rate of mitotic division is indicated in these embryos by the fact that about every other cell in such an embryo shows a c-mitosis. To determine the time at which mitosis first starts, we fixed every 6 hours during this period, again "trapping" mitoses with colchicine, and determined that mitotic activity resumes between 6 and 12 hours after explantation.

The rapidity of inception of mitotic activity suggested that other events might occur even more rapidly during the activation which follows explantation. A likely candidate for such prior changes is the mitochondrion, the residence of the cytochrome enzymes which are known to become reactivated with the inception of postdiapause development. Miss Kaocharern has recently found that the mitochondria of diapausing embryos freshly removed from the egg do not stain with Janus green B, but become stainable within a few hours after explantation, before cell division starts. Since Janus green staining presumably depends on a functional cytochrome system, we are apparently observing histochemically a rapid reactivation of this system after explantation.

These mitochondrial changes were studied further in tissues stained by an acid green–fuchsin technique. The mitochondria stain pink by this method, and, with ordinary optical equipment, the diapausing embryo seems to lack mitochondria. However, closer study with special oil-immersion lenses shows that mitochondria are present during diapause but that they take the fuchsin stain very weakly.

Evidently, then, on the basis of these preliminary results, the mitochondria are present in diapausing embryos but lack a functional cytochrome system. The cytochrome system is regenerated very rapidly following chilling in the whole egg or following explantation of the embryo, and the reconstruction of functionally complete mitochondria is shortly followed by the resumption of mitotic activity. Our next task is to test the various hypotheses we have constructed to identify the nature of the stimulus to restoration of mitochondrial activity and to identify causal sequences of these various events which accompany the inception of postdiapause development. The results which Professor Wigglesworth has just presented on changes in mitochondria during the molting cycle of *Rhodnius* provide a welcome guide for our further studies.

WILLIAMS: I am just wondering about this water business. Have you any thoughts about what is happening there?

BUCKLIN: The change in the mitochondria is a very rapid one, occurring very shortly after explantation. It seems to me that this sort of change would tend to support Wigglesworth's previous suggestion that there is some "releasing mechanism" involved here. The parallel between such a "release" and Holtfreter's "sublethal cytolysis" is, I think, quite plain. It is also possible that explantation by these methods is simply bypassing the normal mechanism of mitochondrial change and is simply bringing the enzyme and substrate together in an unusual way. However, it appears to me to be reasonable at the moment to use as a working hypothesis Slifer's suggestion that the uptake of water which accompanies the inception of postdiapausal development is a causal factor.

WILLIAMS: There seems to be in your data a suggestion that they will react to a twice-concentrated Ringer solution. They could not have osmotic uptake of water; it is worse than having no water at all. So, then, do you think that this is an active uptake, and, if so, what is concerned with it?

BUCKLIN: It is very likely an active uptake of water on the part of the embryo or its membranes. There may be a pump here which is simply unable to function because the eggshell is denying access of water into the egg. We used twice the normal concentration of Ringer solution. The normal concentration of the Belar Ringer we use is 0.16 molar—0.9 per cent sodium chloride, plus other salts.

CARLSON: Of course, we work with younger ones, and we work with different species of *Melanoplus,* but the concentration which is isotonic with a 14-day *Chortophaga* embryo and at least with *M. femur-rubrum* at the same age is about 0.7 per cent. We have found that putting embryos in a hypertonic solution (and Belar's is hypertonic as far as our embryos are concerned) will put these cells in mitosis. All the interphases disappear, and there is a great excess of prophase stages, and this will stimulate mitosis. We get a rise in the rate of frequency of cells going from metaphase to anaphase. If we put them in lower than 0.7 per cent hypotonic solution, they swell, and we have an excess of interphases. It does seem that some of the early phophases revert to the interphases, and we have a lowering of the mitotic rate. I could not help wondering whether anything so simple as withdrawing water from cells by hypertonic solution should break diapause and initiate mitosis.

BUCKLIN: Well, it happens also in solutions which presumably are hypotonic. You remember I showed that cell division recommences in half-concentrated Ringer—0.45 per cent NaCl. In other words, it happens in both cases whether the medium is hypertonic or hypotonic.

WADDINGTON: Work on the activating system in the amphibian embryo shows that certain activators definitely go inside the cell and attach themselves to certain cytoplasmic granules. Is there any similar evidence for any of your insect activators—whether they are operating on the cell surface or whether they go inside?

WIGGLESWORTH: Well, I do not know. The very earliest changes that you can see, of course, are inside the cell.

WADDINGTON: After cells have been treated with ecdysone, can you then show that there is ecdysone within them?

WIGGLESWORTH: That has not been done.

WYATT: We need some isotopically labeled ecdysone.

WILLIAMS: I would like to attempt to pinpoint what I think is our problem. The prothoracic gland hormone has some primary effect—a hypothetical primary action. Now in the diapausing animal or animals which are not growing for one reason or another, we may infer that there are one or more defects in the system prerequisite for growth. When the hormone acts and growth begins, a lot of things happen. Just because some change occurs, there is no guaranty that this change is in the causal sequence of hormonal action. It may be merely a result of growth. I would suggest that, in the analysis of the mode of action of hormones, one needs to show that a change fits in somewhere between the action of the hormone and the initiation of the growth response. Our problem, in short, is to detect the changes which lie in the path of action of the hormone and to dissociate these from all other reactions which are, in point of fact, the result of the growth reactions.

KARLSON: The system is intact, but it does not work. It is blocked by some end product or inhibited by the reactant.

WILLIAMS: The inhibitory theory of diapause does not seem to stand up too well.

BUCKLIN: This inhibitory theory has been suggested, of course, in grasshopper diapause.

KARLSON: No, I do not mean an inhibitory action; I mean a block in the chain of events of an enzyme system.

WIGGLESWORTH: I quite agree. I should like to make one comment on Dr. Bucklin's reference to Holtfreter's "sublethal cytolysis." The view that I was putting forward and the view with which I think Dr. Bucklin is in sympathy is on all fours with that sort of conception. Of course, it did not begin with Holtfreter. The same idea goes back to Loeb in his suggestion for the artificial induction of parthenogenesis, the conception that, by injury of the cell, you are bringing reactants together. That idea, of course, is perfectly familiar to biologists. We are perfectly happy with this idea of cell structure and isolation of reactants and so on. Biochemists have always looked with distaste upon this idea. They like to think of the cell as a test tube, but now in the last few years they are suddenly making the great discovery that living tissues have a structure, and I think that very soon we shall find the biochemists on our side.

WADDINGTON: I do not like the name "sublethal cytolysis" for the processes we are considering, because you can get the sort of thing that Holtfreter was talking about, for example, in the induction of neural tissue in the Amphibia. This neural tissue can be induced perfectly well by substances which stimulate growth. A stimulation of growth can hardly be called a "sublethal cytolysis." What you really mean is that some change is taking place in the metabolism or the structure of the cell which enables an already existing mechanism to start working. With that idea I am in perfect sympathy and put it forth some time ago myself, but I do not think that that mechanism is always something which it is legitimate to call "sublethal cytolysis." If that term means anything at all, it must mean some sort of injury. Injury may pull the trigger, but you can pull it by other means.

RIZKI: The time required for completion of cytokinesis of blood cells of *Drosophila* when there is a high cytokinetic index (around the time of molting) is very short, $2\frac{1}{2}$–3 minutes. If you follow mitosis in vitro when the cells are dividing in between these two high-activity periods, cytokinesis takes a longer time. If the molting hormone is acting around the molting time, it would be interesting to learn whether the cell surfaces change in permeability or the cytoplasm of the cells is affected by the hormones so that cytokinesis occurs at one time at one rate and another time at a slower rate. This might give some clue as to the way in which the hormone is acting upon the morphological units of the cell, and I feel we must find the morphological site.

SCHNEIDERMAN: It is difficult to say this with Drs. Waddington and Wigglesworth in the same room, but I find it hard to think that the triggering of growth by this prothoracic gland hormone can be made analogous to something which you can envision as a kind of stirring around the inside of a cell. Maybe I am interpreting "sublethal cytolysis" wrongly; the hormone is certainly a natural trigger for the events of morphogenesis. Perhaps you can have another trigger. Would you imply that these other agencies are acting like alternative triggers?

WIGGLESWORTH: Yes, but these have to be the same stimuli in principle. The idea that hormones are bringing about their effects by changes in permeability is becoming increasingly popular. Insulin, for example; and the pituitary growth hormone, likewise, is pictured nowadays as producing its action by an effect on permeability.

WYATT: Would Dr. Wigglesworth like to be more specific about an activity involved here? Do you think this might be a question of an enzyme getting to its substrate, owing to changes in the permeability of the cell membrane, nuclear membrane, or other intracellular membranes?

WIGGLESWORTH: I have spent much time gazing down the microscope at these cells and wondering. I have never taken very much interest in the cell membrane. I think it belongs to the people who study echinoderm eggs. I can imagine all sorts of membranes inside the cell at the nucleus, at the nucleolus, at the mitochondria, and plenty of other membranes. I think it is better to keep these ideas vague until one can get some evidence for them.

CASPARI: As Dr. Wigglesworth correctly points out, there are all sorts of membranes on the permeability of which hormones might be imagined to act. In view of what has been said previously, I wonder whether the mitochondrial membrane, which is well demonstrated by the electron microscope, might not be a good candidate for controlling the access of some of the enzymes to their substrate. In looking at mitochondria through the microscope, I have frequently wondered what the conspicuous differences in shape that can be observed may mean in functional terms. One possibility I could think of would be that changes in the spatial relations of the enzymes might influence reaction velocities, even if permeability remains constant.

RIZKI: There has been some study on giant cell formation in fibroblast cells by putting in extracts of tubercle bacillus in tissue culture preparations. There is an indication that these extracts act on the lipids of the cell membranes. And, as I mentioned before, auxins seem to act on the cell walls in plants.

WILLIAMS: Because a thing changes is no guaranty that its action is interposed between the action of a hormone and the biological end result. When an animal develops, everything changes. So it does not suffice to show that a thing changes. One has a larger responsibility to show that the change is necessary for the reaction rather than a result of the reaction.

WIGGLESWORTH: This applies to what we have been saying about cytochrome c. It applies to all these changes, and the question is, Which is the primary change? We are seeing something here which is happening within a few hours of applying the stimulus, and permeability changes are all that I have been able to think of.

WYATT: Another difficulty here is that biochemists are coming more and more to the idea that many of the processes controlling the passage of materials in and out of cells are active transport processes and not due to diffusion. If the hormone affects an active transport process, this is putting it back onto the level of an enzyme reaction.

WIGGLESWORTH: I absolutely agree that we are only pushing the problem further back. I would quite agree to include active processes under the term "permeability." I agree with you entirely.

POULSON: We have heard a good deal about the breaking of the effects of diapause. Perhaps someone has some ideas on how the arrest occurs?

WILLIAMS: During the past year, Dr. David Shappirio, working at the Molteno Institute, studied the changes in enzyme systems at the outset of diapause. He found that the wing epithelium of the freshly pupated *Cecropia* silkworm is full of cytochromes. Within 24 hours, cytochromes c and b become undetectable. They stay this way throughout diapause. In *Antheraea pernyi,* a species which normally does not have a pupal diapause, he got this same collapse of the cytochrome system when he established an artificial diapause by removing the brain of the fresh pupa.

BUCKLIN: It seems to me that the problem of diapause relates to two other problems which have interested embryologists for some time. These are two other examples of stimulation—namely, activation of the egg in fertilization and the stimulation involved in inductive processes. Here a similar sequence of historical events occurred. Investigation concentrated first on the "action system" and then on the "reaction system." The study of the reaction system led to these concepts of so-called "sublethal cytolysis," which undoubtedly is not a particularly happy term. But I think that, with improvement in our knowledge of what the enzymatic relationships are, some closer parallel can be shown between other types of activation and the activation following the termination of diapause. Dr. Wolsky pointed out yesterday the parallel between activation in the silkworm and the termination of diapause. This seems to be a case in point.

WADDINGTON: There is a fairly considerable difference between the induction stimulus in the embryonic development of vertebrates, on the one side, and in the parthenogenesis and the diapause system, on the other side. In both parthenogenesis and the diapause system you are dealing with a single pathway of change, which gets started and then is stopped. In the induction of the neural system or of other organs in vertebrates you are normally dealing with alternative pathways of differentiation, into one or another of which the thing gets switched. If you isolate a piece of gastrula epidermis and do not give it any inhibiting stimulus, it does go on changing into a rather abnormal type of cell, which is not any of its proper alternatives; it is not induced one way or the other. In one case you are merely stopping and starting a single process, and in the other case you have the added complexity that you are choosing one or another of the alternatives. You can induce the cells to be neural tissues, *or* to be epidermis, *or* to be mesoderm, and there is some specific difference between these things.

### EXTERNAL STIMULI AND DIAPAUSE

SCHNEIDERMAN: One of the difficulties in our discussion seems to be that the term "diapause" is being used for all stages of arrested development. It would be of great value if Dr. Lees would give us his very good reasons for believing that a single theory cannot explain diapause.

LEES: First, perhaps, I could reply to Dr. Waddington's comment. I often wonder whether the parallel between induction and determination of diapause is not rather closer than he intimated, because in many of these cases of facultative diapause, for example, external stimuli, such as day length and temperature, act on the insect long before the events of diapause; in the silkworm embryo, for example, the effect is not perceptible until the next generation. However, if it were possible to look closely enough, one might find many physiological and biochemical differences between insects which were later going to lay diapausing eggs, compared with those which were destined to be non-diapause egg producers. I think that the term "determination" can legitimately be applied to this process of decision early in development. With reference to Dr. Schneiderman's remarks, certainly various people have tried to introduce a unitary or comprehensive theory of diapause which would cover all instances known to us, no matter whether diapause occurs in the egg or in the larva or in the pupa or as a reproductive diapause in the adult. It seems to me that such a blanket hypothesis is unnecessary. We like to have these unifying concepts, but sometimes we attempt to unify things which are dissimilar. Thus we know now that in the silkworm, *Bombyx,* the egg diapause is controlled by the maternal brain and subesophageal ganglion. The secretion from the latter, as Fukuda and Hasegawa have shown, induces the eggs to develop as the diapause type. On the other hand, the work of Williams and others has revealed that the brain and prothoracic glands are concerned in pupal diapause. Adult diapause is again different, since there is evidence that reproductive arrests are controlled by the corpora allata and perhaps, more remotely, by the brain. As the endocrine systems concerned vary according to the stage at which the insect diapauses, it seems to me that at the moment these phenomena should be segregated. It is also worth noting in this connection that, although there is good evidence for the existence of a diapause-inducing hormone in cases of embryonic diapause, there is no such evidence with regard to larval, pupal, or imaginal diapause, where the arrest appears to stem from the absence of the appropriate growth hormone.

However, I was going to say a few words about the induction of diapause in mites. We know that in the fruit tree red spider mite the egg diapause depends to a great extent upon the length of day which the developing mite experiences. The curve for diapause induction shows its greatest differential between 12 and 16 hours of light per day. On a short day length all the female mites lay diapause eggs, while on a long

105

16-hour day all lay rapidly developing eggs. What can be said about this photoperiodic response? As we know that the plant is not directly concerned, it is clear that the mite is absorbing light. There must therefore be a pigment system involved. For the characterization of the pigment an action spectrum is a primary requirement. Some progress has been made in this direction. The response curve, in fact, shows that the maximum sensitivity lies in the blue region of the spectrum and that wave lengths in the yellow and red regions are completely ineffective. From this preliminary finding it appears that a carotenoid may be involved. Unfortunately, little more can be said until accurate action spectra are secured.

If we postulate a pigmentary system analogous to rhodopsin in the vertebrate rods, we may imagine the pigment being split into constituent molecules by the action of light, these products then directly influencing a further "effector." However, investigation of light-intensity effects shows that the primary reaction system must be more complex than this, since the law of reciprocity does not hold. Indeed, the photoperiodic response is completely independent of intensity, provided that a low threshold is exceeded. This presumably means that the primary products of the photoreaction are linked up with a further reactant.

I should like to draw your attention to one further feature of the response. In addition to light, the period of darkness is also critical. If we investigate the effects of different combinations of light and darkness, we find that long periods of light are somewhat more effective than shorter ones in suppressing diapause. At the same time, the dark period, which exerts the opposite effect, is more potent still. For example, a short night period of 8 hours is hardly diapause-inducing at all; but a long night period of 12 hours can completely annul light periods of up to 20 hours, so that with this combination every mite lays diapausing eggs. The important role of darkness may be an indication of the reversibility of the photoreaction. In some plants the light response controlling flowering or growth is extremely rapid. This is not so in insects, in which slow timing reactions seem to take place in both light and dark periods. The latter can therefore be interrupted by quite long intervals of light without effect.

I have mentioned a few characteristics of the photoperiodic reactions controlling diapause in mites and insects. Of course, we should like to know where these reactions are going on. Unfortunately, until we have the techniques for illuminating insects locally during their sensitive periods of development, we do not know where to look. The pigment need not be obvious; indeed, it may be so dilute that only the most refined methods could detect it.

BLISS: I have done some work on the effects of light and darkness on regeneration and growth in the crab, *Gecarcinus lateralis*. In constant light, regeneration and growth tend to be inhibited, whereas in darkness these processes are favored. In insects with a facultative diapause, on the contrary, I understand that long day lengths prevent diapause and shorter day lengths tend to induce diapause. One might assume that in light there is a release of a hormone which promotes growth and thus prevents the onset of diapause. Is this not a possibility? In the decapod crustacean, *Gecarcinus*, however, because light results in the inhibition of growth, one might logically expect not an activating hormone to be released during periods of light but an inhibiting hormone. A growth-inhibiting hormone is precisely what has generally been found in decapod Crustacea. This hormone is produced by neurosecretory cells of the eyestalks and is released by the sinus glands. Endocrinologically speaking, probably the most striking difference between insects and crustaceans is that insects synthesize and release a neurosecretory growth-promoting hormone, whereas crustaceans are known to produce and release a molt-inhibiting hormone. Release of these opposing hormones in light would explain some of the contrasting effects of illumination on these two classes of arthropods.

SCHNEIDERMAN: Has Dr. Lees any idea on how stimuli acting in the early stages of development can have the effect of decreasing hormone output 4 molts later?

LEES: I should very much like your views on it. I believe you have been making some experiments along those lines. It is difficult enough to imagine how the message is transmitted in *Bombyx;* but here at least the eggs do not become sensitive until the end of development, when presumably the brain and the other endocrine systems are complete. It is therefore possible to imagine that they carry this information right up to the pupa; but, on the other hand, I understand from Dr. Schneiderman that he has some most interesting results in which these effects are impressed upon developing eggs in the ovary of the mother long before the nervous system and endocrine organs have been differentiated. There the explanation becomes even more baffling.

SCHNEIDERMAN: This has been shown before by Simmonds, of course, in the wasp *Spalangia drosophilae* and published in the *Proceedings of the Royal Society.* We have confirmed and extended these observations in another wasp, *Mormoniella vitripeunis*. Exposing female wasps to 10° C. for 5 days results in most of their offspring entering diapause at the end of the last (fourth) larval instar. It is certainly very curious that the conditions to which a female is exposed during oögenesis and before the egg has been fertilized should tell the neurosecretory cells of the brain of the larva three molts later to turn off. What is the recording system in the egg that transmits this information to the larval nervous system?

HADORN: My student R. Perron investigated the factors which control the development of the "Drosophila-mite" *Histiostoma laboratorium.* He found that the molt which leads from the heteromorphic hypopus-stage (Drosophila-mite deuteronymphe) to the tritonymphe (food mite) can be promptly induced just by the smell of yeast. The smell of vitamin $B_2$ will be active as well. Since the experiments were arranged in such a way that no direct contact of the mites with the yeast was possible and since these stages have no mouth, we must conclude that the stimulus has to act through the olfactory and the nervous system.

## · V ·

## *Histolysis and Tumors*

---

### HISTOLYSIS IN INSECTS

DAY (*presiding*): We are not yet completely out of diapause. There is one extremely important subject which did not come up for discussion yesterday, and we shall have a discussion of it before we get on to the subject of tumors.

WIGGLESWORTH: The point that came up when several of us were talking yesterday evening was one which has not been mentioned, and, although in a meeting like this it is impossible to cover all the ground, it did seem to us that this was a point which should be brought up—that is the question of histolysis. We were considering yesterday the factors which start off growth and development, but the breakdown of tissues in insects is also an extremely important matter. Histolysis used to be put as one of the central features of metamorphosis, and many people regarded it as the initial change. We have given up this idea, since our knowledge of hormones and so on has increased. We know now that you can get metamorphosis with a very large amount of histolysis, or you can get metamorphosis in which histolysis is virtually absent. But the fact still remains that histolysis is an important phenomenon. There are very many examples of it. I should just like to mention three which I have observed and thought about myself. When *Drosophila* reaches the adult stage, it has a perfectly good, healthy-looking fat body brought over from the larval stage. It also has a very inconspicuous imaginal fat body. In the next few days the larval fat body disappears, and the imaginal fat body develops. We have no knowledge of the factors concerned, although there are almost certainly humoral factors of some kind. The second example was the one I mentioned yesterday: the intersegmental muscles in the abdomen in *Rhodnius* which develop only for molting and then, within a very short period after molting, autolyse. In the case of the fat-body cells, the whole cell, nuclei and all, breaks down. In the case of these muscles, the nuclei are not affected. It is only the muscle fibrils which disappear. But it amounts to a very substantial quantity of tissue. This autolysis affects only the intersegmental muscles. The dorsoventral muscles alongside them remain intact and healthy.

109

Now that change is, as we know, brought about humorally. The nerves remain intact throughout this process, so far as one can see. The buildup and breakdown take place in the isolated abdomen when the nerves are separated from their cell bodies. We know nothing about the nature of that control. The third example concerns the thoracic gland. The prothoracic gland produces the hormone necessary for growth and molting, persists throughout the larval stages becoming active in each molting period, but on reaching the adult it undergoes histolysis. In *Rhodnius* the gland cells are perfectly normal on molting to the adult. Within 24 hours they are showing signs of breakdown, and in 48 hours they have disappeared. I shall not describe the experiments that I did on this subject, but only the conclusions. Two factors are concerned in that breakdown. The gland must be exposed to some humoral influence which is exerted at the time of molting, immediately before or immediately after. Once the gland cells have been subjected to that influence, they will break down in whatever medium you put them. But that factor, which we shall call "A," is without effect in causing breakdown if the gland throughout the preceding stage of development has been exposed to what we agreed to call the "corpus allatum hormone." This hormone, as you know, leads to the retention of juvenile characters. One of the juvenile characters is a persistent thoracic gland; consequently, if the gland cells during this preceding period are exposed to the corpus allatum hormone, then the factor A fails to cause breakdown in whatever medium you transplant the gland. I mention these facts to emphasize what a great number of humoral factors there must be in the insect controlling its growth. I have the feeling that these few hormones that we have discussed represent only a very small part of the humoral complex which is controlling growth and breakdown in the tissues.

DAY: This comment on the probability of there being a number of other hormones to watch out for calls for further comment.

KARLSON: We know that the corpus allatum hormone by itself does not affect the cells; in our present picture it is only modifying the action of ecdysone. There are two possibilities: first, that the corpus allatum hormone is modifying the cells in such a way that they react in the larval sense to the action of ecdysone, or, on the other hand, the cells might be prepared to do anything under the action of ecdysone, and in the absence of the corpus allatum hormone they develop in one direction and in the presence of that hormone they develop in the other. Dr. Williams has some information on the time of development and the action of the hormone.

WILLIAMS: In order for the corpus allatum hormone to have any effect, it must presumably be present very early. For example, it takes 21 days to make an adult out of the *Cecropia* pupa. In order for the corpus allatum hormone to have any effect in opposing the progress to the adult condition, it must be there not later than the fourth day. And the earlier it is there, the larger its effect.

SCHARRER: May I bring up the fact that the critical period for the corpus allatum hormone is reached after the critical period of the prothoracic gland hormone. This would really indicate that the prothoracic gland hormone goes to work earlier and is then modified by this juvenile hormone. In Dr. Wigglesworth's papers, as in others, it was pointed out that the critical period of the corpus allatum hormone is considerably later than was postulated by Dr. Williams.

WIGGLESWORTH: Yes, I would agree that that is approximately so; but it is a complicated question on which I have published extensively, and I hesitate to speak about it at length.

KARLSON: Would this not fit with Williams, who shows that, at least after the initial action of ecdysone has taken place, the corpus allatum hormone can modify the reaction? It is not necessary that the corpus allatum hormone be present before.

BODENSTEIN: We now have evidence in *Periplaneta* that at least some corpus allatum hormone is present in the organism during the entire intermolt period, although apparently at a low titer. Whether this is also true for the prothoracic gland hormone, I do not know, but I suspect so. I would agree with Dr. Wigglesworth that an effective prothoracic gland hormone titer is reached before the allatum hormone titer reaches its highest point. But I believe also that there is no stage in the larval period of insects in which the reacting material is completely free of hormone influences. The vigilance of hormones is continual.

SCHNEIDERMAN: Do these two hormones play against each other in any way? I think particularly of the idea of hormonal balance often suggested by Bodenstein.

DAY: Insects show this phenomenon of histolysis to an extraordinarily highly developed degree, and, if this subject is discussed in morphogenesis, insects can contribute to it. What are the differences between two muscles as closely related as the sternal and lateral muscles, one of which breaks down and the other does not? Or how does a phagocyte attack one particular set of tissues and not another? Dr. Bodenstein, you have given a fair amount of thought to this problem; have you any ideas on it?

BODENSTEIN: Dr. Wigglesworth, did you say that the nerves in the degenerating muscles stay intact?

WIGGLESWORTH: Apparently yes; as far as one can see, using methylene blue, they appear unchanged.

BODENSTEIN: So the degenerating muscle still supports a fiber, at least for a certain length of time?

WIGGLESWORTH: The involuted muscle consists of the sheath and the nuclei. It has a very rich supply of nerves ramifying all over it, and there seems to be no change in these between it and the normal muscle, except, of course, that the collapsed muscle appears to be more richly supplied with nerves.

WILLIAMS: Dr. Finlayson, of the University of Birmingham, has some work which shows that if you denervate muscles that normally do' not break down at pupation, they do so then. Therefore, something conveyed by nerves must be quite important in maintaining them.

DAY: How general is this phenomenon? Is it a peculiarity of *Rhodnius*—an adaptation to its peculiar feeding habits?

WIGGLESWORTH: I do not know. I have not looked at many others, but I looked at the bedbug, *Cimex,* which has a cycle of development similar to *Rhodnius,* and it showed the same cycle but in a less striking form; and I have examined the pyrocorid bug *Dysdercus,* which is a continuous feeder, and that also shows the same cycle but in a very much less conspicuous form. It may be much more widespread than one has thought.

SCHNEIDERMAN: In connection with this general problem of diapause, can Dr. Wigglesworth comment on the possible significance of endogenous nervous rhythm in the whole problem of periodic activity in the neurosecretion story? There is some very important work by people in your group—Janet Harker, I think—which is relevant.

WIGGLESWORTH: That, of course, raises this whole question of control of endogenous rhythms of growth and endogenous rhythms of other kinds. That particular work of Dr. Harker's concerns endogenous rhythms of activity, humorally controlled. It points the way possibly to the discovery of endogenous rhythms of activity in glands controlling growth. The sort of thing which Dr. Lees was hinting at yesterday. But, here again, we are launching into a morning's discussion.

#### INSECT TUMORS PRODUCED BY THREE GENES

DAY: It is one "clock" against another. I think we had better leave this subject, because the problem of insect tumors is of considerable interest to a number of us, and Dr. Waddington will give us some of his recent work on the subject.

WADDINGTON: I shall report on some work which has been done in my laboratory, mainly by an Egyptian student, Dr. El Shataury. This started by the analysis of three genes, all of which produce changes that can roughly be referred to as "tumors." They are all mutants which showed up in experiments on mutation rates, when vast numbers of genes were found by some of our colleagues. These genes are not associated with any noticeable chromosome abnormalities and are referred to as "point mutations," insofar as that phrase still has any meaning. One we called "Lethal-malignant," another is "Lethal-no-differentiation," and another is "Lethal-no-imaginal-buds." I may also perhaps say a word about what we call "Lethal-benign," which also produces a tumor with black bodies in the hemocoele. Now the observations have been done so far on the morphological level, and all these genes seem to involve alterations to the "blood-forming organs," or, as we propose to call them, the lymph glands. I shall not go into their structure in great detail, but in our observations, which are based on fixed and sectioned material, we distinguish four types of cells in the lymph gland which roughly correspond to the types of cells which Dr. Rizki has seen in the hemolymph itself. The parallelism cannot be drawn exactly at this stage because we do not have exactly comparable information. There is one type of cell which is particularly noticeable and easily recognizable, one that we call the "hexagon"; it almost certainly corresponds to Rizki's crystal cells. Another kind we call "spheroids"; the greater part of the lymph gland is made up of these, which correspond, I think, to Rizki's plasmatocytes. There is a third class, rather less common, which we refer to as "platelets," and which may possibly be connected with the lamellocytes, though I am not sure about this. And, finally, toward the end of the larval life, we get what we consider a transformation of spheroids into something which, to us, looks in section like spindle cells; these are probably his podocytes. That, I think, is probably the way the two schemes fit together.

In a whole-mount preparation of the lymph gland system from a middle third-instar larva one observes the following: the aorta runs down the middle and turns into the heart; a first pair of two large lymph glands (pericardial cells) runs along the cardia; and second, third, and fourth lymph glands are located farther posteriorly and sometimes fuse together. That is the picture in the fully developed form in the middle of the third instar. In the first and second instars the first pair of lymph glands are pretty large, but posterior ones are extremely small. As I said, there is a very characteristic type of cell which, in material fixed in hot fixatives, in the early stages stains very darkly; the cytoplasm is nearly as basophilic as the nucleus; and in later stages, in the later third

113

instar, the cells turn very definitely black and become melanized. These are the cells we call "hexagons." Now one of the major points I want to make is that you find, in various parts of the larvae, pockets of these cells, which look pretty well fixed in place. They are not completely floating and are certainly very closely attached to the matrix of the tissues. They show much the same histological picture as these lymph gland cells, and I propose to refer to them as "oikocytes." "Oikos" is apparently the Greek for "founding a colony," and thus "oikocytes" seems suitable as a general name.

One place where we find these cells is, for instance, in the optic region of the cephalic imaginal buds. In an early first instar, the optic imaginal bud has a nice optic nerve leading to the beginning of an optic glomerulus, but at that time there are no mesoderm cells associated with the bud. By the middle of the second instar, or even late in the first and in the beginning of the second, special cells are very definitely associated with the imaginal bud, and these cells look extremely like the hexagons in the lymph glands at that stage. Now, a bit later on—that is, very late second instar—many more of these hexagon-like cells are associated with the bud. They are associated with the peripodial membrane and appear also under the optic region of the cephalic imaginal bud. By a late third instar, at the time when the cells in the lymph glands show the blackening reaction, the cells associated with the optic bud also blacken in exactly the same way in hot fixatives; and, at a slightly later stage than that, the cells apparently disintegrate. You see nuclear degeneration, and eventually you can see gaps in the tissue where the cells have disappeared. Just at the time when they are showing this melanization reaction and eventual degeneration, you can begin to see the first sign of ommatidia. In the epithelium lying immediately above the hexagons in the optic region, groups of cells are seen in suitable sections. These oikocytes raise a number of questions which I shall mention in a minute.

The same phenomenon occurs in the region where the esophagus goes into the proventriculus. About the end of the first instar and the beginning of the second, one finds oikocytes in the crevice between the esophagus and the proventriculus. From their first appearance they look like the cells in the lymph gland, and at the late third-instar stage they show the same melanization reaction, appearing as large cuboidal blackened cells. Then, just after these cells start showing this blackening reaction, the top end of the proventriculus becomes basophilic, forming the so-called imaginal ring of the imaginal foregut. Now in a section from a Lethal-no-imaginal-bud there is a precocious disappearance of the oikocytes and the hexagon cells. They have also disappeared from the lymph glands, and the development of the imaginal ring is much feebler.

A third place where there is possibly an oikocyte group of this kind is in the testis. This is relatively easy to see in the late larval stage, very shortly before puparium formation. At the caudal end one finds a group of degenerating cells and at the front end two groups, and quite regularly one observes these definite places of cellular degeneration. That was what we spotted first. If you go back to slightly earlier stages, you can see groups of cells staining rather differently in the same position.

In the early second instar it is not so easy to distinguish these cells, but there seem to be groups of cells here which look somewhat different from the main spermatogonia and spermatocytes of the testis. That, then, is morphological evidence which tends to suggest that there are groups of cells in various organs showing the same histological picture as the lymph gland cells and, I think, probably derived in some way or another from the lymph gland. We believe that the lymph glands release cells into the hemocoele periodically, toward the end of each instar. Unfortunately, I do not have a proper slide showing the breakage of a lymph gland and the release of cells. It is a very quick process, and it is not easy to get sections of this occurrence. But we have a slide at about the stage of the second to third molt, which shows what we should consider to be a lymph gland partly regenerating or refilling itself after emptying itself of cells. At some stages you can get the lymph gland almost completely empty of cells, the cells having been discharged into the hemocoele.

In the regeneration of the lymph glands there are mitoses, but I have not made any study of their numbers; cell division must be an extremely quick process. Those phenomena raise the question of what the oikocytes are doing. Their histological behavior shows that they must come from the blood cells in one way or another, either straight out of the hemocoele or from the lymph glands through the hemocoele. Are they exerting any influence on the tissues in their immediate neighborhood? They seem always to be near places where the imaginal rudiments undergo differentiation preparatory to metamorphosis.

Now to go on to one of the tumor stocks, Lethal-malignant. The major unusual occurrence in Lethal-malignant is the appearance of an enormous number of cells in the hemocoele along the ventral nerve cord. They are mainly spheroids from the lymph gland. The spheroids released from the lymph gland also go into the imaginal buds, and they appear to erode them, pushing their way right into the bud itself. Now the point here is the great proliferation and the filling-up of the hemocoele

115

with cells. Enormous numbers of them accumulate in the posterior end of the body, where they find their way in amid the fat body. These larvae often do not pupate until about 3 days after the normal pupation time. Now the cells migrating along the nerve cord—all these groups of proliferated cells, in fact—eventually begin to show an inhibition which eventually leads to degeneration of various kinds. The hexagon cells melanize. Another process which tends to bring their spread to a halt is the transformation of spheroids into spindle-shaped cells, which tend to encapsulate the cells near them. Finally, in the latest stages of these larvae you get a very general transformation of spheroids into spindle-shaped or flatter cells, which become extremely melanized, and a great deal of black pigment is deposited, showing up even without fixative; and in this way you get these black bodies, in this case usually firmly anchored to the tissues which have been penetrated by the cells.

That whole set of processes can be interpreted in terms of two opposite tendencies—the tendency for proliferation of lymph gland cells and a tendency to prevent proliferation, either by the melanotic degeneration or by encapsulating the groups. I think you can see tendencies of both these types also in the normal wild type. In this you get some proliferation of the lymph gland at the end of each instar, and at the end of the third instar you get, in addition, some signs of the restrictive tendencies shown by the melanization of the hexagons and by the transformation of some of the spheroids into flatter cells. So it looks as though in this tumor we have an exaggeration of the normal proliferative tendencies and a relative weakening of the normal tendencies to restrain growth.

Let us turn, now, to another lethal, the Lethal-no-differentiation. It produces tumor-like bodies of quite a different character. Everything goes perfectly normally until the middle of the third instar, when the picture becomes highly pathological. Normally, the gland would be full of healthy-looking cells, but one finds here a lot of degenerating cells and spaces where cells have degenerated. The next abnormality is in the mesoderm of the imaginal buds. The imaginal wing bud of the third-instar larva has a folded epithelium, and we know, more or less, where that comes from. Underneath that are a number of mesoderm cells. Now one finds in the Lethal-no-differentiation that this mesoderm has grown up through the epithelium of the bud, broken it, and spread out into the peripodial sac. This process eventually destroys the imaginal bud. In other cases the proliferation is even more pronounced, and the mesoderm around the bud gives many cells in the hemocoele in the immediate neighborhood of the bud. It is because of this overproliferation of mesoderm that the imaginal buds degenerate and no pupal differentiation occurs. That is one of the pieces of evidence which might lead one to suggest that not only the hexagons associated with the optic buds but possibly all the mesoderm associated with the imaginal buds come from blood cells and the lymph gland. Now that is a suggestion that one would like to find some way of testing properly. The histological picture is compatible with it and slightly suggests it, but does not do much more. There is nothing specifically recognizable about these smaller spheroids and platelets, and you cannot recognize them for certain in the way you can hexagons. Unfortunately, you cannot do the simple thing of transplanting lymph glands into other larvae with a label of some kind, because the lymph gland is one organ which, in our hands, if transplanted, becomes melanized and the cells clump together and die. One can transplant the black bodies, but they are practically dead anyway.

The other lethal I just want to mention is the one we call Lethal-no-imaginal-buds. In section, in an exaggerated case of Lethal-no-imaginal-buds, one finds the brain but no imaginal buds whatever, but it varies, and in many cultures you do find them. The sections also show that when there is no optic imaginal bud, there are no glomeruli in the brain. But the point I want to make is that the mid-gut is full of cellular debris of various kinds and all the caeca are filled with debris; it is this material which blackens, as we shall see later, and which forms the "tumor" in this case. It differs from the imaginal bud tumor or the malignant tumor. Sections of the posterior end of the mid-gut, at a later stage, in which the cavity has been occluded by cellular proliferation, show enormous masses of yeast and bacteria in the gut, and blackening occurs on the outside of the gut. We think that this proliferation has a number of components in it. One thing that happens is a hypertrophy of the cells of the gastric epithelium itself. In normal development, you can find a transitory stage toward the end of each instar, with signs of hypertrophy of the gastric epithelial cells. The free border of the cells becomes highly basophilic, and then you find in the lumen of the gut large lumps of basophilic cytoplasm that appear to have been thrown off from the gastric epithelium. It seems to us that one of the aspects of the gut tumor is an exaggeration of this periodic hypertrophy of the normal gastric epithelium. But that is not the whole story. A section through the stomach wall in a normal early second instar shows the peritrophic membrane and the main gastric epithelial cells; lying underneath them, against the basement membrane, there are a number of small groups of deeply staining cells which are the imaginal rudiments.

117

Now different components of this system may be affected in different gastric tumors. In Lethal-no-differentiation it seems to be mainly a hypertrophy—an actual enlargement of the gastric epithelial cells, with a breaking-off of portions of them, but there is also some proliferation of these imaginal mid-gut rudiment cells. In some of the Lethal-malignant cases these imaginal mid-gut cells are the main things that proliferate.

Lethal-benign is very like the lethals studied by Oftedal. The hemocoele becomes full of blood cells, which change into spheroidal or flatter shapes and agglomerate in a mass that becomes melanized. In my view, all these melanotic black bodies are either dead or moribund.

This is my factual material; now for the main questions. First, what is the function of these oikocytes in stimulating the ommatidial rudiments and the imaginal ring in the proventriculus, and so on? What is the origin of the mesoderm of the imaginal buds? Then there is the question raised by Lethal-no-differentiation—Does the lymph gland enter into any sort of hormonal setup which controls the growth of the imaginal mesoderm? How far can the tumors of Lethal-malignant be considered as a disturbed balance between tendencies to proliferation and tendencies to prevent it? Finally, there is the question of the periodic hypertrophy of the gastric epithelium even in the normal condition and its exaggeration in Lethal-no-imaginal-buds. What is known about the periodic hypertrophy of gut epithelial cells, presumably somewhat parallel to the hypertrophy of the hypodermis? These seem to be a series of problems which this work brings to one's attention. I also believe that one would find out quite a lot in looking for the answers to them.

KARLSON: I have only one question. In Lethal-no-imaginal-buds are the ring glands active, or are they inactive, as in the case of Lethal-giant larvae?

WADDINGTON: I cannot say anything about the ring glands; the larva does not get beyond the middle of the third instar.

SCHNEIDERMAN: I am not convinced that the word "tumor" should be applied to the things we have been talking about. How do you delimit the word "tumor"? There are all kinds of abnormal growth. And the use of the words "malign" and "benign"? Do you use those in the loose sense? Would these tumors satisfy the criterion of vertebrate pathology as far as transplantability and reproduction in other hosts are concerned?

WADDINGTON: I have always taken it that "tumor" is essentially a widely defined word that could be used for any abnormal growth. The words "malign" and "benign" I use in a pretty loose sense. The parallelism between these *Drosophila* tumors and vertebrate tumors—I think

118

you have to be very, very cautious about that. Malign does invade tissues, whereas Benign stays as a relatively isolated black body in the hemocoele. Benign can be transplanted, and it persists as a surface upon which other blood cells can accumulate. Malignant, if transplanted, immediately turns into a melanotic black body, like all these cells from the lymph glands.

WIGGLESWORTH: Regarding the function of these cells, it is very dangerous, of course, to argue from one insect to another, but it might be relevant to say a word about hemocytes in general. In the first place, there are probably several sorts. Many of the sorts are probably just differences in shape of the same cell, but beyond that there are real differences. In *Rhodnius* there is a very considerable proliferation of hemocytes during the molting cycle; hence they are doing something in connection with growth. Exactly what they are doing we do not know. They are cells which have clearly a very active metabolism. I have a lot of sympathy with the idea of Cuénot which goes back sixty years, that these are to be regarded as unicellular glands concerned in the production of blood constituents, quite possibly blood proteins, and perhaps other constituents of the blood. That is all hypothetical, but it might give a hint as to what these cells are doing when they aggregate in the regions of actively growing tissues.

The other point is more definite. Besides these hypothetical functions, the hemocytes in *Rhodnius* contain glassy droplets, which are strongly PAS-positive, not digested by ptyalin; they appear to be neutral mucopolysaccharides; and these cells during the molting cycle accumulate upon the basement membrane and can be seen to be discharging this material to add to the substance of the basement membrane. I believe that they are often responsible for forming the mucopolysaccharide membranes which surround the fat body, the muscles, and so on. If you look at a transverse section of a newly forming muscle, for instance, in the last molting stage of *Rhodnius,* in the thorax, you will find every cleft in between the muscle fibers occupied by one of these cells, discharging this mucopolysaccharide material to form the sheaths around the fibers. That is another function which these cells might constantly be performing around the growing tissues.

SANG: In the Oregon K wild-type *Drosophila* the flies which hatch from a culture after the first 2 or 3 days frequently have benign melanomas which are not genetically determined and are presumably due to some nutritional deficiency. In fact, most nutritional deficiencies on synthetic media result in an increase in these melanomas, so that their appearance is a non-specific stress symptom, as Oftedal implied. Is it not

119

likely that the melanization part of this process is the insect's immunological response to the presence of surplus, probably dying, cells? Salt's
work suggests this, and, if so, may we be concerning ourselves too much
with things which only look alike and which are not always tumors in
any real sense?

WADDINGTON: Yes, I think I said that in normal development the
lymph gland cells have a tendency to become melanized and to degenerate and clump together, and almost anything, as you say, will increase
this and produce actual visible black bodies in the hemocoele. They
seem to be less interesting than tumors of cells that are overproduced
before they become melanized.

DAY: Did I understand that you consider that the origin of all the
tumors that you were discussing is from blood cells, with the possible
exception of the mid-gut tumor?

WADDINGTON: Yes, they come from the lymph gland cells. There are
some cells in the hemocoele during most of the larval life, but whether
they are all from the lymph glands is difficult to determine. If some of
them are, it seems simpler to suppose that they all are, until there is
evidence to the contrary.

BODENSTEIN: The only evidence that the blood cells come from the
lymph glands is that you find these big black hexagon cells first in the
lymph gland; later you find them in other places. Is not this the main
argument? Is it not possible that these black cells which go into these
different regions also go into the lymph glands? What you assume to
be coming out might be going in. I should like to know more about the
origin of the mesoderm. It seems hardly possible that it could come
from the blood cells.

WADDINGTON: I should like to ask Dr. Poulson about the origin of
the lymph glands. Is there any lead from the embryology?

POULSON: Although the separation of the mesodermal rudiments in
the early embryo is very clear, many details of the later differentiation
of particular mesodermal tissues remain to be worked out in *Drosophila*. When I was working on the embryology of the ring gland, it became
necessary to distinguish between its rudiments, which are ectodermal in
origin, and two groups of cells lying just behind them, close to the anterior aorta. These cells—about a dozen in number, derived from anterior thoracic mesoderm—are soon covered with a thin sheath and are
the rudiments of the lymph gland or blood-forming organ, as it has also
been called. I referred to them as "pericardial glands," as their function was even more speculative at that time than now. As Dr. Rizki has
very beautifully shown, the number of these organs increases during the

larval stage, and the cells in them parallel very closely certain of the types of blood cells floating in the hemolymph with regard to both morphology and mitotic behavior. Dr. Rizki's observations and the lack of any direct evidence for release of cells from the lymph glands during the larval stage suggested to me that these may be essentially imaginal organs and that their cellular contents may be released only during metamorphosis. Whether these are the source of imaginal mesoderm cells other than blood cells, as you have suggested, Dr. Waddington, is certainly an intriguing question. If we could find a mutant with no lymph glands paralleling your Lethal-no-imaginal-buds, the answer might be given quickly.

The question of the origin of the mesoderm is an extremely difficult one. I have no direct evidence myself on the origin of the imaginal mesodermal tissues. The question is whether the mesoderm of the adult is derived from the discs themselves or from cells not originally invaginated with the discs. I believe that mesoderm cells of the adult are not directly derived from the discs, while Dr. Rizki thinks otherwise. The only thing that I can say is that some cells, presumably from what we call "larval mesoderm," become associated with the imaginal discs and become the muscles and so forth of the adult; but which cells I do not know. They are extremely tiny at that stage.

On the other hand, the longer one looks at the details in *Drosophila,* the more one begins to see. Things that I could not see ten or twenty years ago now stand out so obviously that one can scarcely understand why he did not see them then!

WADDINGTON: What we want is a nice gene that labels mesoderm— then we ought to be able to get some somatic mutations to recognize the epidermis separately from the mesoderm, but I do not know such a gene.

RIZKI: I was examining the mitotic patterns in undifferentiated imaginal discs, and I think that if the imaginal disc cells have the potentialities to differentiate and orientate in different directions, why cannot these cells give rise to the mesoderm? They are dividing cells. Now I think it is an unnecessarily complicated hypothesis that the mesoderm does not originate from the cells of the imaginal discs themselves but comes from somewhere else.

WILLIAMS: It is true that the imaginal discs are very simple epithelial structures. They fold up in a complicated way, and then one sees the mesodermal stuff appearing there. And to me it is a fascinating notion that this may come from a distant place. It is rather reminiscent of the migration of neural crest material in the vertebrate embryo. I would like to ask Dr. Hadorn whether, in the overlapping fields of the genital discs, he thinks that the epithelial part is crucial or that the mesoderm is crucial. Dr. Wigglesworth has emphasized many times that in insects it seems to be the ectoderm, the epithelium, that shapes the insect, whereas I believe that in the vertebrates it is thought that the substratum underlying the epithelium is more crucial.

HADORN: If one implants imaginal discs from Lethal-giant larvae into normal hosts, one should expect normal cells to invade the implanted disc. But we never got any normal development from imaginal discs of Lethal-giant larvae in a normal host. This does not, however, disprove your theory, because we transplanted not earlier than into the second instar and this might be too late.

WADDINGTON: According to this interpretation, all the mesoderm is coming from essentially the same place and goes to different imaginal buds, where it must then be given its local character, presumably by the ectoderm.

GEIGY: If one treats the polar plasm with ultraviolet, the whole mesodermal part of the gonad is still formed, and you get well-differentiated male and female gonads but devoid of genital cells. That means that in the case of the gonad there are certainly two origins— the polar cells formed on the posterior pole on the outside of the ectoderm and two groups of mesoderm cells forming the rest of the gonad. This gonad is reached later by the imaginal disc forming the genital apparatus of the fly. I have been very much interested in seeing the testis which Waddington has shown us—the hind part where he pointed out that the oikocytes penetrated just the part left after castration. When the polar cells did not reach the mesodermic part of the gonads, I found gonads very much reduced in size, and just this hind part was left. This is, perhaps, an interesting picture of the origin of these cells.

HADORN: What about the gonads, Waddington? Should we not expect some mixed ones in gynandromorphs where male and female cells "would invade the gonads"? You think the oikocytes do not differentiate at all, but just degenerate?

WADDINGTON: I am not offering any speculation of whether these oikocytes have anything to do with sex determination. They certainly degenerate in the third instar, but whether before that they have done anything to start the gonads to make the spermatocytes or spermatogonia I do not know. However, there is no evidence that they have anything to do with deciding whether it is a male or a female.

WILLIAMS: You may not be able to transplant these glands, but can you extirpate them?

WADDINGTON: I think it would be very difficult to extirpate them completely. But one of the things we do want to do is to injure them; I think you probably could, either by Strahlenstich (UV) or by cauterization, with only a moderate amount of injury. We pulled out the genital discs. But you have a whole set of those lymph glands lying right against the aorta. They are not nicely isolated, like other discs. I was wondering whether there was likely to be any future in injecting India ink, trypan blue, or one of those things?

WIGGLESWORTH: Well, that might reveal what I call hemocytes. I have some sympathy with Dr. Rizki's view that genuine mesodermal cells may well be differentiating from the epidermis. That is a pure guess. But mixed up with these and quite indistinguishable when you look at them in sections are large numbers of what I would call hemocytes, derived from elsewhere in the body fluid.

WADDINGTON: It is quite possible, but so far I believe that there is more evidence for the presence of the hemocytes than there is for your postulated genuine ex-epidermal mesoderm.

### INSECT TUMORS INDUCED BY THE SECTION OF A NERVE

DAY: There are still other sorts of tumors which we have not discussed yet. Dr. Scharrer will present some ideas on these.

SCHARRER: I should like to crystallize some of the problems instead and stimulate some discussion, particularly on some of the pertinent questions that Dr. Schneiderman raised this morning. If you study insect tumors, you find several types, in addition to the *Drosophila* tumors so far discussed. But what we really want to know is whether these are tumors in the true sense as understood by specialists in mammalian pathology and what the characteristics of true tumors are. And you may guess right away that I am the last person to attempt to answer such a question, but there are certain points which came up in Dr. Schneiderman's questions: first, Are these tumors transplantable? I might say that there is very little known about any invertebrate tumor with respect to this point. However, if you read the vertebrate literature carefully, this is not an essential criterion. Second, the question of metastasis; even that is not a criterion which the pathologist insists upon. I know of hyperplasias among mammalian tumors which metastasize, and I know of truly malignant tumors which do not. So we do not have to worry too much about these points. One point, however, comes up again and again in the characterization of any tumor, and that is its differentiation from what we call "overgrowths," such as hyperplasias (some people call them "injury reactions" and so on), on which point Dr. Day has contributed, for example. Tumors usually show a considerable degree of cellular transformation into cell types of a kind different from those from which the tumors originated. This is an important point, and it is the only one I want to illustrate in mentioning the tumor with which I have worked; that is, the tumor in *Leucophaea* which can be induced by the section of a nerve. In the slides you can see that there are, for example, two very large cells, perhaps even a binucleate cell, which is very different from all the rest of the cells; this will serve to illustrate my point. The small oval nuclei are rather similar to those of the cells of origin of this mid-gut tumor, namely, nuclei, as they appear in the epithelial cells of the mid-gut, and the large cell is one which is definitely characteristic of this tumor. This, then, is one criterion characteristic of the tumors I have been describing in insects. A second point has to do with the general problem of the relationship between nerves and the tissues which are innervated by these nerves. My reason is that I still have not gotten over the remarkable observation of Dr. Wigglesworth, that you can see nerves supplying muscles that, in essence, do not exist at times when you can demonstrate the nerves. Further study on this unique observation will bear on the general problem "What does the nerve do when it innervates a tissue other than stimulate it in the classical sense?" For those who do not know the work in *Leucophaea,* let me say that the method of induction of the tumor is by severing a nerve. This is a case, then, where we have to study the trophic action of nerves on tissues, and in this particular case its absence leads to abnormal growth. Unfortunately, we do not know much about the details; we should like to know, for instance, what chemical substance it is that, when present, prevents this abnormal overgrowth. This tumor is rather unique so far as tumor formation is concerned, but it is not unique if viewed in the larger frame of reference, as just pointed out. The incidence of the tumors in *Leucophaea* is around 75–80 per cent. We do not have a great deal of evidence on other species. I am going to try *Blabera* soon.

BODENSTEIN: We have tried *Periplaneta* and used perhaps twenty individuals. These animals were observed for 6 days to about 5 weeks after the operation, but we never found any effect.

SCHARRER: Since it takes sometimes only 5 or 6 days, sometimes several months, to develop the tumor, your time of observation may be too short. Also, I think you would have to have about at least two hundred or three hundred specimens to be absolutely sure.

SCHNEIDERMAN: This is exceedingly interesting because in the other cases when nerves play a role in growth it is a trophic action of the nerve (e.g., in amphibian regeneration and in the development of adult silk moths). This seems to be an example of an antitrophic action of nerves; i.e., normal innervation restrains abnormal growth.

SCHARRER: I am not sure that I denervate the tissues, but I have not been able to demonstrate a second type of innervation. The nerve I section is autonomic, from the stomatogastric nervous system, and there could be hyperstimulation of the tissue when an inhibitor is removed. I do not know.

WILLIAMS: I wonder whether you would like to comment on the neoplastic properties of this growth?

SCHARRER: The term "neoplasia," I understand from pathologists, does not necessarily mean malignancy. I have thought for a long time that the tumor may acquire malignant characteristics, but, if anyone proves the contrary, I shall be glad to accept his evidence. This tumor can become extremely invasive, and it can develop so far as to destroy the cuticle and so penetrate the body wall. That, of course, leads to the death of the animal, but usually the animal dies even before that happens. I have tried to see whether the death of the tumor-bearing insects may be due to starvation, because, after all, we are dealing with a gut tumor predominantly, and I have determined in a crude manner the fat content of whole animals, done carbohydrate analyses, nitrogen determinations, and so on and have compared these results in tumor-bearing and in starving animals, and the former die much sooner than any depletion of reserves in the body would warrant. Another interesting aspect is a tie-up with the hormonal situation. The mortality, but not the incidence, is much higher in the female than it is in the male group. If you produce the tumor in castrates, that is, if you cut the nerve several weeks after castration in both sexes, then the two mortality curves resolve into one which is intermediate. In other words, after castration the sex-related mortality is no longer observed. The hypothetical sex hormone perhaps has something to do with this.

WIGGLESWORTH: Do you see any relation between your results and Pflugfelder's on corpus allatum extirpation?

SCHARRER: I first observed these tumors after corpus allatum extirpation, and I thought I was dealing with the same phenomenon. Later I found that the tumors had nothing to do with the hormonal disturbance caused by allatectomy but rather were the result of the section of the recurrent nerve. At this point I checked Pflugfelder's papers again to see whether the same situation might have occurred in his experiments, but this is not the case. The tumor-like growths Pflugfelder observed in his material are actually caused by the absence of the corpora allata, a fact which is demonstrated by the result of re-implantation of these glands. In his case this led to the prevention of abnormal growths, in mine it did not.

BODENSTEIN: And in Pflugfelder's work, I might add, not only gut tumors but other types of tumors—ovarian tumors, epidermal tumors, etc.—appeared.

HADORN: Is there not some connection with the work of Hamburger and Levi-Montalcini?

SCHARRER: Very briefly, this work concerns the effect of tumor tissue on the nervous system. The group in Hamburger's laboratory replaced the anlage of a limb in the chick embryo by sarcoma, and these implants stimulated nerve growth over quite some distance, so that not only the tumor tissue became heavily innervated but also a number of other organs which at this stage are normally still devoid of innervation. When sarcoma and nervous tissue were placed next to each other in tissue culture, an impressive invasion of the tumor by outgrowing nerve fibers was observed. The substance in the tumor which apparently stimulates nerve growth has been purified to a certain degree. In a sense, these studies represent the reverse of my own observations.

RIZKI: Do these animals that have been operated on allow the normal passage of food through the gut?

SCHARRER: For a long time, yes, but not in the extreme cases. When you look at some of the tumor tissues you see clearly that they can no longer absorb or secrete. Frequently, as I have said, the tumor animals die sooner than that, so that the death of the animal cannot be due solely to its inability to digest food.

RIZKI: We have been implanting pieces of larval middle mid-gut of *Drosophila* into adult hosts in the course of some experiments, and when the peritrophic membrane is left inside the implant, the gut heals at both ends. If yeast cells are present in the lumen of the implanted gut, these cells can continue their growth, and when you remove the implant, you can see many micro-organisms growing in there. I was wondering whether it is possible that the passage of food is not normal after operation on your cockroaches. After a while, could there be an infection of the micro-organisms which could produce a diffusible product, such as phenolic substrates, a source of melanizing material (tumor-forming)?

SCHARRER: We have studied the hind-gut, and I have found changes in it due to infectious agents. These changes never resemble these tumors, but they do resemble the hyperplasia that Dr. Day has described.

GEIGY: I do not know the technique you used for operation, but can the nerve regenerate, invade the part where the tumor is formed, and stop its spread?

SCHARRER: That would be extremely interesting, but I have never been able to devise a way in which this can be tested. You cannot tell from the outside whether the animal has a tumor. What we would like to do is re-establish innervation, but so far we have not succeeded. What you suggest would not account for the basic result, but it would be an interesting thing to do. We should like to look into the animal with a "window" which would show the tumors, in order to follow tumor development.

SCHNEIDERMAN: Does anyone have an idea why all these reagents that are so effective in producing abnormal growths in mammals are so completely ineffective in insects?

DAY: This is a relevant question, but I hope it does not stop all discussion on Dr. Scharrer's tumor. Are there any ideas on this question?

WILLIAMS: I have never known a tumor to be produced by carcinogenic agents in insects. I remember some years ago screening all the carcinogenic substances in Professor Fieser's laboratory, in animals that lived as long as 2 years thereafter. And, regardless of the endocrine situation in the insect, the carcinogenic agent had no effect.

WADDINGTON: Hasn't Jack Schultz recently reported inducing tumors in *Drosophila* by feeding them in some cases with antivitamins and in other cases, I think, with carcinogenic agents?

BODENSTEIN: One can get tumors in flies, as was pointed out here before, with all sorts of nutritional upsets.

WIGGLESWORTH: In *Rhodnius* the nearest approach to a tumor that I have been able to see has been in indolent wounds. In rather gross injuries you can get an overgrowth of epidermal cells which become multilayered and do not join up nicely with their neighbors (and I might say in parenthesis that these multilayered structures of ectodermal origin look extremely like mesoderm!), and you feel that in this process they might well turn into a tumor. These structures contain the most astonishing giant cells with hundreds of chromosomes in the metaphase plates and multipolar spindles; but eventually all this goes, order is restored, and you get a continuous layer.

SCHARRER: In *Leucophaea* you get the same transformation of epithelial cells into what looks very much like a connective tissue tumor. As a matter of fact, a number of pathologists have identified these (on looking at my slides) as sarcoma-like, and yet I am quite sure they are epithelial in origin.

DAY: This brings us back to the most important problem that Dr.

Scharrer raised, which is the phenomenon of the transformation of the cell type. I think it is true that insects have, more than any other group, a polymorphic array of blood cells which is quite extraordinary. I should like to ask what, in your opinion, the origin of these tumor cells is and whether there is any possibility that they might be blood cells that have got in there.

SCHARRER: I just say that I am more and more thinking of the possibility that blood cells may enter into the picture, and for that reason I was very much interested in Dr. Waddington's discussion this morning. I am sure that the early phase of this growth occurs in the epithelial cells. It might well be that blood elements enter the growths, but of the fate of these cells I am not now prepared to speak.

HADORN: Do you know whether the tumors start from one single cell, or do they originate at different places?

SCHARRER: I have evidence that they start at more than one place, because I have early stages where small separate tumors are present.

DAY: But this nerve innervates a number of different points, and if you have degeneration occurring at these points, will not blood cells settle down there?

SCHARRER: That is a point which must be taken up seriously, I agree.

BODENSTEIN: Does the nerve not fork? If you cut only one of the forks, you would get less disturbance of nerve supplies, and you should get fewer nests of tumor formation.

SCHARRER: I have cut one fork, but this is an extremely difficult operation, and I must admit that I have not enough successful cases to answer this question quantitatively.

RIZKI: The fat-body tissues (shown in slides) are free of blood cells before they are invaded by the latter. I cannot understand how the blood cells get in between the other cells, but there they are, and it is therefore possible that they get in between other kinds of cells. In a preparation stained with periodic acid Schiff, after amylase treatment when glycogen had been removed, one sees in between the fat mass these lamellocytes going in. The blood cells can infiltrate between other cells.

BODENSTEIN: Dr. Wigglesworth, does not this picture look very much like the one you observed when these cells penetrate between the muscles?

WIGGLESWORTH: It is exactly like the entry of the hemocytes between the muscles to form the sheaths; and you get the same change among the fat-body cells too. But I do not quite see the relevance to this problem.

SCHARRER: If I understood correctly, you meant that the blood cells may enter into the gut tissue. I am certainly convinced that blood cells can pass through tissue membranes, but I have observed very early stages of the transformation of the epithelial cells of the mid-gut.

DAY: This is a very important point because it brings us back to the view that all insect tumors may originate from blood cells.

SCHNEIDERMAN: But if the epithelium of the gut is showing such early changes, it suggests that it is very probably contributing to the tumor.

SCHARRER: If Dr. Day implies that these changes are due exclusively to invasion by blood cells, then I would not agree. This is why I emphasize that the results of Dr. Waddington are in line with our observations. There may well be blood elements entering into the formation of the tumor. I have, however, no evidence that the blood cells alone account for the origin and further development of the tumor.

BODENSTEIN: After the tumor is formed, there is a bad spot in the gut, and the blood cells would aggregate there.

WADDINGTON: Certainly, in one of those lethals I showed, the primary origin of the tumor is not the blood cell but the gastric epithelium.

GEIGY: Is there a technique for staining the nerve terminations in order to find them again after the operation and to see whether the beginning of the tumor is always at the nerve terminations?

SCHARRER: The very fine nerve terminations are no longer stainable. If we observe the end point in a fine branch, how do we know that this is really the end? This difficulty of impregnating fine terminal fibers applies to methylene blue as well as silver preparations.

HADORN: Would it be possible to stimulate these gastric nerves electrically?

SCHARRER: Somebody should do it, but I am not too well acquainted with the techniques. Dr. Cohen at Harvard is doing a little work along these lines, and I hope that he is successful.

WYATT: In certain sawflies you have mid-gut tumors produced as a result of virus action. There are some polyhedral viruses that invade groups of mid-gut cells and cause proliferation. After metamorphosis these neoplasms become necrotic and are sloughed off into the hemocoele and remain there. Dr. Bird at Sault Ste. Marie has studied this.

SCHARRER: I am familiar with this work. I have no evidence in my work that viruses are involved. It could be that each cell contains viruses and that denervation activates them, but I have no evidence for such a possibility.

129

WYATT: I was not suggesting that, but this is just another case of tumors in insects.

WILLIAMS: Along this same line I have from time to time found rapidly growing tumor masses in *Cecropia,* highly metastatic, rapidly spreading through the animal, great nodular masses, soon killing the animal. They are transplantable, etc. I can say that in every case, upon examination of this neoplastic development, the tissues show the presence of Sporozoa. And I often wonder what would have happened to me if I had not been able to see these Sporozoa.

DAY: It is clear that there are striking differences between the cells in vertebrates and those in insects, and there seems to be no reason to assume that the tumors resulting from them are, in fact, comparable. The indications that carcinogenic substances have no effect would substantiate this, and the nervous factors, which Dr. Scharrer has shown, also bear on it. The recent trends in the role of viruses in tumors have not been studied in insects, and the field is still wide open.

# · VI ·

## Regeneration

---

### FACTORS CONTROLLING REGENERATION OF LEGS AND MOLTING
### IN LAND CRABS

SCHNEIDERMAN (*presiding*) called on Dr. Bliss for a report on her study of regeneration and molting.

BLISS: I shall discuss three points which may be of particular interest to those who are working with insect material: a comparison of the endocrine control of growth in insects and crustaceans; the morphology of the regenerating crustacean limb; and the use of the regenerating limb as an index of crustacean growth and of the growth-controlling influence of certain environmental factors, namely, illumination and temperature.

In the land crab, *Gecarcinus lateralis* (Fig. 8, *A*), neurosecretory cells occur in the brain and eyestalk. Also in each eyestalk is a storage organ called the "sinus gland." Neurohormones are apparently synthesized within the bodies of neurosecretory cells in the eyestalks and brain and are then transferred to the massed fiber endings, the sinus glands, where they are stored and later released into the circulation. Several years ago a French scientist, Gabe, described paired structures, the Y organs, which later were reported by Echalier to secrete a growth-promoting hormone in the crab *Carcinus*. According to Gabe, the Y organs are analogous to the prothoracic glands of insects.

Comparing crustaceans and insects, we know that the hormone produced by the neurosecretory cells in the protocerebrum of insects is an activating hormone; the corresponding hormone in crustaceans, originating within neurosecretory cells of the eyestalk ganglia and of the brain, is an inhibiting hormone. Neurosecretory storage organs in crustaceans are called the "sinus glands" and in insects the "corpora cardiaca." In insects it is known that a hormone, synthesized within neurosecretory cells of the brain and transported to the corpora cardiaca, activates the prothoracic glands when released into the circulation. In crustaceans it has been suggested that a substance released into the circulation by the sinus glands may inhibit the activity of the

131

A.

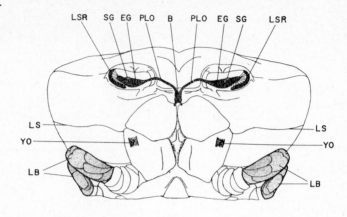

B.

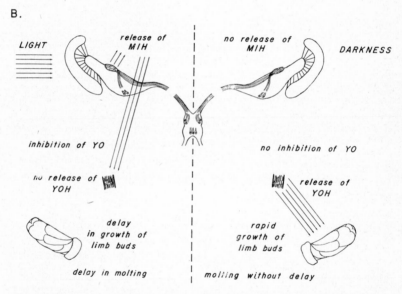

FIG. 8.—*Gecarcinus lateralis*. *A:* Anterior aspect of this crab, showing the principal components of the neuroendocrine system believed to be in control of premolt limb regeneration and molting. *B*, brain; *PLO*, optic lobe peduncle; *EG*, eyestalk ganglia; *SG*, sinus gland; *LSR*, light-sensitive region of eye; *LS*, epimeral line of suture; *YO*, Y organ; *LB*, limb buds. *B:* Hypothetical plan for the control of premolt limb regeneration by the neuroendocrine system. This schema applies only to the stage of premolt limb growth that can be reversibly inhibited by light (see Fig. 11). *Left side:* Impact of light on light-sensitive region of eye results in (1) synaptic stimulation of neurosecretory cells in the X organ of the eyestalk and in other parts of the central nervous system; (2) release of molt-inhibiting hormone (*MIH*) from the massed fiber endings, the sinus glands; (3) inhibition of the Y organs (*YO*) by *MIH*; (4) withholding of growth-promoting Y organ hormone (*YOH*) from the circulation; (5) delay in premolt growth of limb buds; (6) delay in molting. *Right side:* In darkness, with retention of *MIH* within the sinus glands, the Y organs release *YOH*, limb buds grow rapidly, and molting occurs without delay.

Y organs (Fig. 8, *B*). Hypothetically, only when this inhibitory product is withheld from the blood stream or is reduced below threshold concentration, can the Y organs release their growth-promoting substance, which seems to be comparable to the growth-promoting hormone from the prothoracic glands of insects.

Such is the growth-controlling neuroendocrine system in crustaceans, as it compares with that in insects. Next I shall discuss regeneration in a crustacean. Morphological studies performed by Mary H. Hodge at Radcliffe College on the regenerating limb of *G. lateralis* have shown that when the dactyl, the most distal segment of a limb, is injured, this animal does not autotomize its limb. On the contrary, provided that there is sufficient time before molt, a small, hooklike protrusion (Fig. 9, *A*) is formed from the next segment, the propus. When the limb is

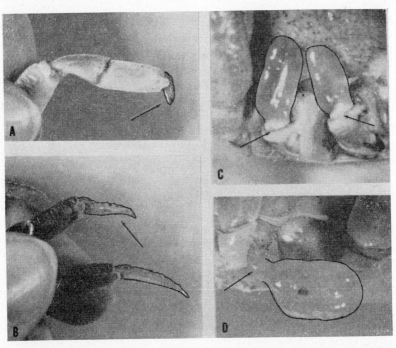

Fig. 9.—*Gecarcinus lateralis.* *A*, cast exoskeleton of walking leg bearing at the distal end of the propus a protrusion (*arrow*) in which a dactyl (see *B*) was formed prior to molt. *B*, regenerated dactyl (*arrow*) which at molt was removed from the old exoskeleton of walking leg shown in *A*. A normal unregenerated dactyl is shown below. *C*, normal limb buds (*outlined in black*) formed on the autotomy plane (*arrows*). Note close apposition of these limb buds with body of crab. *D*, limb bud (*outlined in black*) formed from a regenerated coxa (*arrow*). Note projection of limb bud from the body at a sharp angle. (*A* and *B* from preparations by D. E. Bliss; *C* and *D* from preparations by M. H. Hodge.)

133

removed from the old exoskeleton at ecdysis, a complete dactyl is visible (Fig. 9, *B*). In other words, the crab has constructed a dactyl within the hard protrusion from the segment just proximal to it. Sometimes a new dactyl develops within the proximal tip of the propus, and no protuberance from the propus is visible. When either of the two segments immediately proximal to the propus is injured, the limb is generally autotomized; that is, it is reflexly detached at a preformed breakage plane or autotomy plane located near the base of the limb in the basi-ischium. Subsequently, a folded limb bud develops externally on the autotomy plane (Fig. 9, *C*). If a limb is injured proximal to the preformed breakage plane, in the region of the most basal segment, or coxa, the animal devotes at least one entire intermolt to the construction of a new coxa (Fig. 9, *D*). A striking difference exists between a limb bud formed upon a regenerated coxa and a normal limb bud developed at the autotomy plane. The former, lacking an articular connection with the coxa, cannot be moved as can a normal limb bud and protrudes from the body at a sharp angle (Fig. 9, *D*). A normal limb bud, formed on the autotomy plane, can be held close to the body (Fig. 9, *C*) and can easily be moved by means of a joint between the coxa and the basi-ischium.

In *G. lateralis,* regeneration of a limb can occur most rapidly and completely at the preformed breakage plane or at levels immediately proximal to it. Comparable observations by other investigators have been made on several crustaceans. This is in contrast to the situation prevailing in many insects, where, according to Bodenstein, the principal factor determining the capacity for regeneration may be the amount of tissue remaining after amputation rather than an inherent gradient of regenerative potential along the axis of an appendage. Although, commonly, some regeneration of a given appendage may occur in insects at any level of amputation, in the limbs of certain species (e.g., *Rhodnius prolixus*) the regenerative capacity increases in a distal direction, and regenerates formed at proximal levels may be diminutive and feeble.

Finally, I shall discuss the manner in which the rate of growth of a regenerating limb formed on the autotomy plane has been used in one species of crustacean as an index of over-all growth and of the influence of environmental factors on growth. It is possible that certain modifications of our techniques may be useful in the study of growth in insects.

In *G. lateralis* a measurement is made from the autotomy plane to the tip of the limb bud. Length of limb bud divided by width of carapace, times 100, results in a figure called the "*R* value." The rate of change in *R* indicates the extent to which over-all growth is occurring. In a non-growing crab, the *R* value may remain relatively constant for many months. If eyestalks are removed, however, there is a rapid rise in the value of *R,* due to a rapid increase in size of the limb bud (Fig. 10). Limb growth is terminated just prior to molt. The limb buds of a crab with eyestalks may develop only to a certain point, characterized by a low *R* value, and then regeneration may cease or may continue very slowly in several short steps. When, however, preparations for molt begin, the limb bud of this animal grows rapidly to an *R* value which is characteristic of the particular limb and of the particular species of crustacean. For instance, the second walking leg of

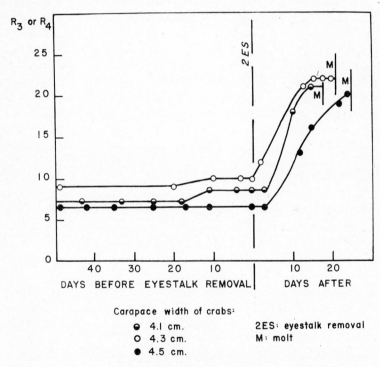

FIG. 10.—*Gecarcinus lateralis.* Induction of premolt limb growth by bilateral eyestalk removal.

$$R = \frac{\text{Length of limb bud}}{\text{Width of carapace}} \times 100 \, .$$

Subscript for *R* indicates appendage used, $R_3$ for the third walking leg, $R_4$ for the fourth. The responses of these three crabs are typical; many other experiments of this type have given similar results.

*G. lateralis* may reach an *R* value of 28 before molting occurs, but its fourth walking leg does not attain an *R* value greater than 24.

On the basis of the observations just described, we have divided limb regeneration in *G. lateralis* into three stages (Fig. 11). The first stage, called "basal growth," occurs soon after autotomy. It seems to bear no relationship to the endocrine state of the animal and is not indicative of imminent molt, for this type of limb growth can occur at any time in the intermolt cycle and even under unfavorable environmental conditions. It appears to be a form of localized growth. Next there is a "growth plateau," during which the value of *R* may remain constant or may increase stepwise ("advancing growth plateau"). During advancing growth plateau the value of *R* may reach 10 or possibly higher. Finally, there is "premolt growth," which occurs only just prior to molt and consequently indicates that molt is imminent.

I shall now briefly discuss data from eleven normal specimens of *G. lateralis* which were placed at a temperature of 28° C. (approximately the summer temperature within their burrows in the Bahamas) after they had first been exposed to a temperature (34°) of mild stress (Fig. 12). Following autotomy, the crabs had completed basal regeneration at 34° and had then stabilized at growth plateau. This indicates that at 34° conditions were not favorable for molting. When maintenance at 34° was in darkness and subsequent maintenance at 28° was also in darkness, all three crabs subjected to these conditions regenerated rapidly at the lower temperature and molted. When two crabs maintained in light at 34° were moved to darkness at 28°, they also rapidly completed premolt regeneration at 28° and molted. Two crabs placed in darkness at 34° and subsequently in light at 28° underwent premolt regeneration at 28° somewhat more slowly and eventually molted, but one crab under these conditions neither completed premolt regeneration nor molted. When three crabs were in light at 34° and subsequently in light at 28°, their transfer to the lower temperature seemed to stimulate regeneration briefly, but premolt limb growth soon stopped and during the entire period of observation (78 days) there occurred no molting. These results suggest that both the removal of a thermal stress and exposure to darkness favor premolt growth.

The important role played by light in the control of premolt limb regeneration is shown even more clearly by the results of the next experiment. With a temperature of 28°, adequate moisture, and the privacy of a separate jar, *G. lateralis* when placed in darkness tends to undergo rapid premolt regeneration and to molt (Fig. 13). On the other hand, when a crab is maintained at 28° in light, basal growth is

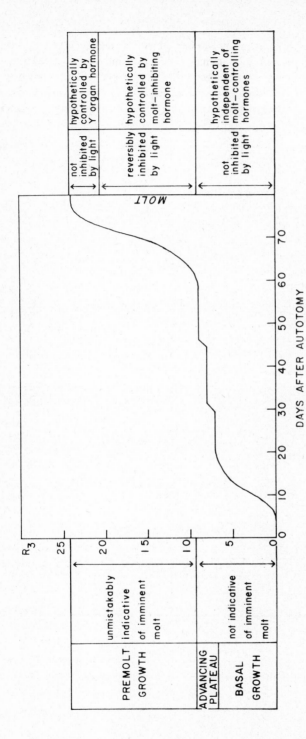

FIG. 11.—*Gecarcinus lateralis*. Idealized curve to show typical stages of limb bud growth from the autotomy plane. For derivation of *R* see legend for Fig. 10. Premolt limb growth, if it commences in darkness as assumed in this figure, can be reversibly inhibited by light, except in its terminal phase. If, however, premolt limb growth originates from a long growth plateau due to prolonged inhibition by light (see Fig. 13, *open circles*), it cannot be inhibited by further exposure to light.

usually followed by growth plateau. When the growth plateau is eventually terminated, premolt limb growth takes place as rapidly as if there had been no prolonged period of inhibition. It appears that inhibition of premolt limb growth by light, once overcome, cannot be reinstated. Possibly the Y organs have been irreversibly triggered. Echalier has recently reported that removal of the Y organs from *Carcinus maenas* causes both regeneration and molting to halt and that reimplantation of the Y organs into the same crab starts these processes once again.

The situation is actually somewhat more complicated than it may appear to you at this point. When the crabs have recently arrived at the laboratory, they are refractory to the growth-promoting influence of darkness. Each crab, whether in darkness or in light, shows a growth plateau, but the growth plateaus of crabs in darkness are terminated earlier than are those of crabs in light. On the contrary, after maintenance in the laboratory for many months, crabs in constant light may

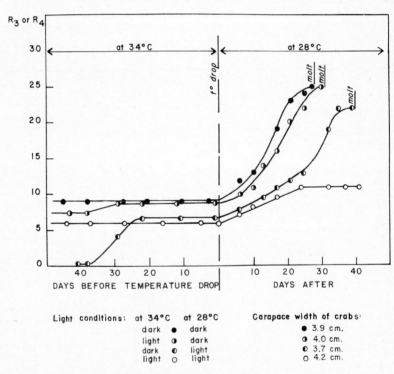

| Light conditions: | at 34°C | at 28°C | Carapace width of crabs: |
|---|---|---|---|
| dark | ● | dark | ● 3.9 cm. |
| light | ◑ | dark | ◐ 4.0 cm. |
| dark | ◐ | light | ◒ 3.7 cm. |
| light | ○ | light | ○ 4.2 cm. |

Fig. 12.—*Gecarcinus lateralis.* Induction of premolt limb growth by a drop in temperature. These curves are typical of the responses shown by eleven crabs. Details are presented in the text. For derivation of *R* see legend for Fig. 10.

show no growth plateau and may regenerate as rapidly as do crabs in darkness.

Another experiment tells more concerning the responses of these crabs to light and darkness. A limb of a specimen of *G. lateralis* was autotomized and permitted to regenerate. When growth plateau had been reached and it was clear that premolt growth was not imminent, the crab was carried from the light chamber into the dark chamber. Premolt growth started. The crab was carried back to the light chamber, and regeneration stopped. Return of the crab to darkness caused premolt growth to start again. The next exposure of the crab to light caused regeneration to pause only briefly. It appears that when premolt limb regeneration is almost complete, it can no longer be inhibited by light, possibly because of an irreversible activation of the Y organs, which remain in control from that time until molt (Fig. 11).

The results of preliminary experiments with implants of central nerv-

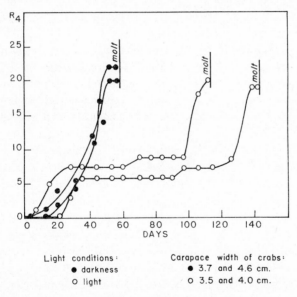

Fig. 13.—*Gecarcinus lateralis.* Long delay in premolt limb growth (*open circles*) during exposure to constant light. Note that, once growth plateau is terminated, premolt limb growth in light takes place as rapidly as in darkness (*closed circles*), and the slopes of the premolt growth curves are similar. The responses of these four animals are like those of most crabs which have been in the laboratory 2–3 months before use. However, crabs recently arrived may show a growth plateau in constant darkness, and crabs long maintained in the laboratory may have no growth plateau in constant light. For derivation of R see legend for Fig. 10. (Reprinted from Bliss, 1956. *In:* Bertil Hanström: zoölogical papers in honour of his sixty-fifth birthday, ed. K. G. Wingstrand, p. 62 [Lund, Sweden: Zoölogical Institute].)

ous tissues located in the eyestalks have been interesting. If the contents of an eyestalk are implanted into a regenerating crab, premolt regeneration halts, sometimes for 2 or 3 weeks, a period of time which probably represents the life of the implant. Only if implantation takes place during the final phase of premolt growth, are eyestalk tissues ineffective in causing regeneration to cease.

Inhibition of premolt limb growth by light appears to be mediated through the neurosecretory system, with the release by the sinus glands of a molt-inhibiting hormone. In darkness this hormone is apparently not released (Fig. 8, *B*). Since the inhibitory effects of light can be duplicated in either normal or eyestalkless crabs by implantation of eyestalk tissues, it would appear that the light-reversible period of growth is controlled by the neurosecretory system. Final premolt growth is not light-reversible and may be entirely independent of neurosecretory control (Fig. 11).

Mary Hodge has found in *G. lateralis* that during basal growth there occurs differentiation of striated muscle fibers, motor and sensory neurons, apodeme, and epidermis and that some demarcation into segments is taking place. During growth plateau, further development of muscle fibers and of motor and sensory neurons occurs, while demarcation into segments becomes more pronounced. Final differentiation of the tissues of the regenerating limb takes place during premolt growth.

SCHNEIDERMAN: Has Dr. Lees any comments on the photoperiodic reaction?

LEES: I think the parallel with insects is rather remote. In most insects you might say that more light in the form of a long day length results eventually in the continuation of development, not the inhibition of growth, although we do have insects that behave in the opposite manner. An example is *Bombyx,* in which shorter periods of light promote diapause-free development. Then from conversation with Dr. Bliss I understand that light is perceived through the eyes of this crab, whereas in insects there is no definite evidence that this is the pathway to the receptors. In the only insect so far examined, the silkworm *Anthercea,* the ocelli of the larva can be cauterized without changing the response. The light receptors are unknown. The differences are, therefore, rather striking. I should like to ask Dr. Bliss whether this behavior has any particular function in nature.

BLISS: It is not likely that in nature the critical factor for this species is illumination, since burrowing into the ground is always a possibility and the interior of burrows provides darkness. It is more likely that for this land crab availability of moisture is the key factor. Certain experiments in the laboratory tend to bear this out.

KARLSON: The hormone of the Y organ is most probably closely related to the insect hormone, because extracts from Crustacea can cause pupation in *Calliphora*. It is important to know whether the early stage of basal growth would correspond with the hormone. Probably it should not.

BLISS: It probably should not. It seems to be more of a local response, by means of which the tissues of the limb are prepared for the time when premolt activities will commence.

KARLSON: Do these crabs have a chromatotropic hormone in the eyestalk, and is the release of this affected by darkening the eyes? This would introduce another hormonal factor whose function we do not know.

BLISS: I have not been able to interpret the changes of color in *G. lateralis*. In the first place, a large part of the exoskeleton is heavily pigmented. Chromatophores can be clearly seen only in the posterior portion of the carapace and in the limbs. The posterior portion of the carapace may be orange, gray, blue, or almost any color. One point, however, is quite clear. When eyestalks are removed, the posterior portions of the carapace and the limbs usually become orange and remain so. A normal animal, on the contrary, alters its color pattern in these areas.

I should add one remark about the number of hormones. Limb regeneration is completed 3–5 days before molt. Since *G. lateralis* is a land crab, it takes in water before molt and stores the water in some form within two diverticula of the pericardial cavity, called the "pericardial sacs." Before molt these become very swollen. It is particularly interesting that this uptake of water does not occur until limb regeneration is essentially completed. One wonders whether the hormone which is regulating water balance and that which controls limb regeneration are identical. Carlisle has postulated that in *Carcinides maenas* the hormone which controls water balance and that which inhibits molting are different.

BODENSTEIN: I do not quite understand the relationship between the different growth periods and the hormones.

BLISS: I would suggest that the intermediate phase of premolt growth, which can be modified by implants of portions of the central nervous system, may be regulated by the neurosecretory system. I would further suggest that the final phase of premolt growth may occur when the Y organs, which are supposedly analogous to the prothoracic glands, have been irrevocably triggered. Limb regeneration henceforth appears to be irreversible.

BODENSTEIN: I understand that the first period is not affected by hormones. This, I think, is very confusing because a lot of growth and differentiation must go on here.

BLISS: The reason why I think that basal growth is not affected by hormones is that the conditions under which the animal is maintained seem to be of no consequence. The crab can be at a temperature of 28° or at 34°, in darkness or in light, in moisture or in dryness, in a single jar or in a community tank. It makes no difference. The factors which appear to be capable of preventing premolt growth do not appear to hinder basal growth.

BODENSTEIN: After this plateau, what hormone comes in?

BLISS: The Y organ hormone, which is supposedly analogous to the prothoracic gland hormone. From my results it would seem that the Y organ hormone may be in control of growth when limb regeneration is no longer reversible by light. Thus far, this is only a theoretical possibility.

SCHNEIDERMAN: Dr. Scharrer, would you like to say anything about this?

SCHARRER: Let us forget for a moment about the inhibitor from the eyestalk; then we have a system completely parallel to that in the insect, namely, a neurosecretory hormone which triggers the equivalent of the prothoracic gland; in the crab, the trigger from the eyestalk would come after the plateau. The critical period of the Y hormone has been reached at that last break, when the situation is no longer reversible. The stimulator from the neurosecretory cells is first and causes the Y organ to release its hormone.

BODENSTEIN: Do I understand that the hormone of the neurosecretory cells stimulates the Y organ; then growth occurs and, after a certain stage is reached, the Y organ ceases to function?

SCHARRER: Right. But this is still too simple. Now, unfortunately, we cannot be too sure about the Carlisle hormone, the one which stimulates the Y organ. The other point which comes up is that the inhibitor is presumably also produced by neurosecretory cells, but by a different type of secretory cell, likewise located in the eyestalk. Perhaps it helps the insect people to understand this complicated system if we speak of a kind of diapause. The molt-inhibiting hormone delays molting but may not altogether prevent it.

WADDINGTON: Do I understand that the limb always goes back to its normal size when growth can occur? If that is so, does it not mean

142

that the limb itself is a factor in controlling the molt? Why does the molt not occur before the limb is ready?

BLISS: I do not know. Indeed, why does not the molt occur before the new exoskeleton is complete? Limb regeneration is only one of the changes occurring before molt.

WADDINGTON: One might argue that the time relations are adjusted so that the time that it takes for the gland to produce enough hormone is just enough for the integument to go through its appropriate changes. But here a limb has got to do a great deal more than an integument normally has to do. Presumably, the growth-promoting action has to go on longer, so that regeneration can catch up to the normal size. If the limb gets back to its normal size, then it would seem to me that the limb itself must be part of the system.

WIGGLESWORTH: There are two points which I should like to make. The first is a general one. I am rather skeptical about things being "triggered." The analogy of the trigger is that you explode a small charge which instantly sets going a big one, and it is an all-or-none reaction. I do not know about this material, but in the *Rhodnius* material I certainly do not think that is so. You get visible evidence of the effect of the thoracic gland hormone within a few hours after feeding; therefore, the brain hormone must already have been liberated shortly after feeding; and yet the insect can be decapitated, and molting fails to occur up to $2\frac{1}{2}$ days after feeding. In the case of the thoracic gland hormone or using purified ecdysone, you can titrate the animal; giving 1 $\mu$g., you get so much muscle fibril synthesis and so much cell swelling; 2 $\mu$g. give a little more, and so on until you get the process complete. There is no evidence of triggering; I think Dr. Karlson has observed similar effects.

BLISS: I think that the term is appropriate. During the last phase, when limb regeneration appears to be irreversible, the Y organs may have become irreversibly activated. Previous to this point, they presumably have been either inactive or intermittently active.

WIGGLESWORTH: Well, yes, in *Rhodnius* you can get a point where you can decapitate between, say, $2\frac{1}{2}$ and 3 days. You can say that by that time the glands have been triggered. They have been set going at an earlier stage and have now reached a point where a sufficient stimulus has accumulated.

The second point is this: I have not thought about these results closely, but I do not see why this small amount of growth which you are getting, this basal level which does not go on to molting, should not be due to very small subthreshold quantities of your Y organ hormone.

143

BLISS: It may be due to that. However, it is not indicative of an imminent molt.

RIZKI: What method do you use for measuring the growth length of the regenerating limbs? If you take the volume into consideration, does this growth curve change?

BLISS: I do not know; I have not checked it. When we first studied limb regeneration, we considered the advisability of determining the volume of limb buds. Since we were not trying to study limb growth per se, we decided to use linear measurements as the basis for our indices of growth. Linear measurements are less laborious, and they have proved quite useful for our purposes.

HADORN: Can the tissues store hormone? If that is so, then the whole curve becomes simple.

SCHNEIDERMAN: If this is so, what makes the tissues decide to grow after they have stored hormone for a long time?

WIGGLESWORTH: There is, of course, good evidence that the corpus allatum hormone can be stored, but I do not know of any evidence that the molting hormone is stored.

O'FARRELL: It seems that the crab and, I think, other Crustacea also regenerate a limb which is entirely as good as new, that is to say, in size and also in respect to the number of segments. Yet in cockroaches, which I think are about as good regenerators as any insects you can find, you always have a deficiency of one tarsal segment, and, oddly enough, you always have a deficiency of one cercal segment in regeneration. Now this suggests that there is some peculiar difference in the morphogenetic pattern of the regenerate which does not run to completion, and it never runs to completion, no matter how many molts it has, whereas, in Crustacea, regeneration can apparently be completed in one growth cycle.

BLISS: In Crustacea a regenerated limb is usually shorter than a normal limb. At each subsequent molt it gradually increases in size until it is as long as the corresponding limb on the other side. But the regenerate seems to be morphologically complete at the first molt. At least, there is nothing obviously missing.

REGENERATION OF APPENDAGES OF THE GERMAN COCKROACH

O'FARRELL: Reviewing the work so far done by Dr. Stock and myself on regeneration in *Blattella,* I should stress that we have confined ourselves to inflicting injuries of a kind quite likely to be sustained by the animal in nature—i.e., loss of a leg at the plane of weakness, loss of a cercus from its base, and loss of a tarsus by pulling off.

The trochantero-femoral articulation, although traversed by a band of muscles running through into the femur from their insertion on the wall of the trochanter, constitutes a natural plane of weakness at which the leg comes off in response to gentle pulling on the femur or tibia; it seems to be a plane of autospasy rather than autotomy. Detachment of the leg at this plane may lead to several effects. Before the "critical period" (i.e., the point in the intermolt period at which the onset of the next ecdysis is irreversibly determined), this procedure leads to the appearance at the next ecdysis of a completely differentiated regenerate, which is (and subsequently remains) short of one tarsal segment; this regenerate is at first smaller than the normal leg but approximates to it in size during subsequent molts. Simultaneous removal of both legs of the pair results in the appearance of symmetrical regenerates, not smaller than those arising from removal of only one leg, at the next ecdysis. Removal of one leg or both legs simultaneously *after* the critical period results in the appearance of one papilla, or a pair of papillae, at the next ecdysis; regenerates do not appear until the second ecdysis after the operation. The papilla is often considerably smaller than the normal trochanter when the operation is performed a short time after the critical period, i.e., well before the next ecdysis is due.

If the two legs of a pair are removed in succession, further possibilities arise. Removing the first one well before the critical period and the second a little later gives rise to an asymmetrical pair of regenerates at the next ecdysis. Removal of the second leg at a later stage gives rise at the next ecdysis to a regenerate from the first operation and a papilla from the second. Removal of the first leg after the critical period results in the appearance at the next ecdysis of a more or less asymmetrical pair of papillae, that from the first leg removed often being smaller.

Tabulation of the delays in ecdysis associated with various timings of leg removal in relation to the critical period shows the following: (1) No delay in ecdysis is associated with the appearance of one or two papillae. (2) The appearance of a single regenerate at the next ecdysis after removal of the leg is associated with a delay approximately equal to the time elapsed between the animal's last ecdysis (or eclosion from the egg) and the operation. Operations performed on the first day of the instar give rise to a delay in ecdysis of about 1 day, like those performed on the second day of the instar. Simultaneous removal of both legs gives similar results. (3) Successive removal of both legs followed by the appearance of two regenerates at the next ecdysis is associated with a delay in ecdysis approximately equal to the time elapsed be-

145

tween the last ecdysis (or eclosion) and the second operation, while the appearance of a regenerate and a papilla is associated with a delay in ecdysis approximating the time elapsed between the last ecdysis and the first operation.

The time relations between operation and ecdysis thus follow a pattern conforming to the "all-or-nothing" principle whereby either a regenerate is produced, with delay in ecdysis, or a papilla without such delay; but intermediate conditions between regenerate and papilla, with a reduced delay in ecdysis, are extremely rare.

By repeated removal of a regenerated leg each time it appears, complete regenerates are repeatedly produced, but the number of molts undergone before metamorphosis is increased, usually by only one or two, sometimes by as many as six, a complete regenerate being produced and removed at each of these molts. Repeated regeneration and the supernumerary instars associated with it have no recognizable effect on the morphological features or reproductive capacity (so far as investigated) of the animals concerned, at least when the number of supernumerary instars is small. Nothing is known of the reproductive capacity of the animals undergoing three or more supernumerary instars, but only one case of obviously juvenile morphological characters has been noted, in an animal metamorphosing at its twelfth ecdysis (controls have six or seven ecdyses from eclosion to metamorphosis).

Regeneration of a leg involves replacement of much muscle tissue. The cercus, however, is devoid of intrinsic muscles and can be totally removed without causing any damage requiring extensive replacement of muscle. Regeneration of the cercus does not follow an all-or-nothing principle; a graded series of conditions is seen, ranging from healed cuticle to a fully formed regenerate, deficient only by a segment when compared to the normal cercus. The extent of regeneration seen at the next ecdysis depends upon the time elapsing between the operation and that ecdysis, which is at most only slightly delayed; the critical period observed in leg regeneration is not operative. If a metathoracic leg is removed before the critical period, simultaneously with a cercus, the resulting increase in duration of the period available before the next ecdysis leads to the appearance of a substantially larger and more complete cercal regenerate than can be produced without the delay in molting occasioned by leg removal. Thus the regeneration of a leg and that of the cercus are apparently independent of each other and are not antagonistic or competitive processes. The very small delay in the next ecdysis associated with cercal regeneration is comparable in magnitude with the delay in the second ecdysis after removal of a leg beyond the

146

critical period, with production of a papilla at the first (undelayed) ecdysis after its removal. In both these instances, the delay is approximately doubled, although still very small, when both members of the pair of appendages are simultaneously removed. It is not yet possible to say how far these observations on cercal regeneration are applicable to the situation at metamorphosis, when the cerci, unlike the legs, are subject to major morphological and possibly functional changes. This is now under investigation.

The tarsus of the leg is essentially a hypodermal and cuticular structure without intrinsic musculature, but it has a somewhat larger volume than the cercus. If pulled off, the tarsus brings with it the pretarsal retractor apodeme and a substantial quantity of attached muscle. A regression and reorganization of tissue in the tibia follow, and ultimately a new tibia is formed inside the old one, with a distal space occupied by a regenerated (tetramerous) tarsus. Regeneration occurs on an all-or-nothing principle related to the critical period in the same way as regeneration of the leg from the trochantero-femoral joint. Delays in ecdysis occur with single, simultaneous, and successive regeneration of tarsi in much the same way as that described for the leg, but the magnitude of these delays is smaller, the time lapse between tarsal removal and next ecdysis being approximately 70 per cent of the duration of the normal instar instead of nearly 100 per cent.

A preliminary examination, to be confirmed by detailed histological study, of the sequence of events in leg regeneration from the trochantero-femoral joint has brought out the following main points: (1) The early stages of regeneration are accompanied by a very pronounced local molt within the stump (coxa plus trochanter) of the leg. The hypodermis withdraws from the cuticle far up into the coxa, and the great coxal muscles slide back along the apodemes of the trochanter, which become extensively exposed within 48 hours of the operation. A dense column of cells, probably mainly hypodermal in origin, simultaneously appears, surrounding the stump of the main trachea of the leg. This is the blastema. (2) The coxal muscles then undergo considerable degeneration, while the blastema begins to differentiate from the proximal end. Some migration of cells between the degenerating coxal muscles and the blastema seems to occur. The articulations of the regenerate appear in a strictly *proximo-distal* sequence, and there is no sign of any segmentation of the tarsus until all the proximal articulations are formed and organized muscles have begun to appear in the femur and tibia of the regenerate. The foregoing account applies only to regeneration occurring after removal of the leg before the critical period. (3) If the leg is re-

147

moved after the critical period, the local molting described in 1 does not occur; some blastema formation seems to take place within the papilla if sufficient time is available before the next ecdysis. The sequence of events described in 1 and 2 does not begin until after the ecdysis and shows the somewhat surprising difference of *disto-proximal* differentiation of the blastema. Tarsal segmentation is well advanced by the time that the proximal articulations are fully formed, and muscles are beginning to appear in the femur and tibia of the regenerate.

These observations, so far as they go, lead us to wonder whether they are reconcilable with the belief that one single hormone is responsible both for molting and for growth and differentiation. The time relations between regeneration of the leg or tarsus and the molting cycle seem explicable only in terms of some influence of regeneration on the humoral mechanism controlling molting. If the localized molt and the growth and differentiation of the regenerate make demands on the available supply of molting, growth, and differentiation hormone, and thus delay ecdysis, why is the delay so insignificant when a cercus is being regenerated, and so great when a leg is being replaced? Why does repeated regeneration, in which presumably the alteration of hormone balance associated with regeneration is greatest, have so little effect on the anatomy and function of the animals? If they had a relative excess of juvenile hormone, this ought to be expressed by the appearance of "nymphoids," of which we have observed only one in some hundreds of animals studied. The possibility seems to exist that two different interrelated systems are involved in regenerating largely muscular structures, like the leg, and hypodermal structures, like the cercus. By facilitation of its response to a subthreshold hormone concentration already present in the blood, by nervous stimulation, or by some other means, the regenerating leg or tarsus, with muscle involvement, is able to affect the molting cycle as the non-muscular cercus does not. A leg blastema differentiating in the milieu provided by an animal which has had its ecdysis postponed through leg removal before the critical period differentiates proximo-distally, forming its muscular regions first; in the milieu of an animal whose ecdysis has not been delayed (i.e., following the appearance of a papilla at the next ecdysis after operation) the differentiation is roughly disto-proximal, with the muscular parts developing much later in relation to the non-muscular tarsus. Even in normal molting, we have some indications that the muscles are visibly affected before the hypodermis, certainly well before the occurrence of hypodermal mitoses indicates the general onset of the molt. Is it possible that the effects of the molting hormone may be largely specific to muscles, serving mainly as a trigger for general hypodermal growth and differentiation, whose actual course is determined by other causes, including the generally accepted interactions between "juvenile" hormone and "growth and differentiation" hormone?

SCHNEIDERMAN: Dr. Bodenstein, would you care to comment?

BODENSTEIN: I think that the factual observations are more or less like mine. I cannot time my animals as well because the intermolt periods of *Periplaneta* vary enormously. At this point, I think it is appropriate to point out that even an adult leg of *Periplaneta* is able to regenerate, provided that certain conditions are fulfilled. For instance, if one transplants an adult leg into the prothoracic shield of a nymphal host and then amputates the transplant within the autotomy joint, a new leg appears after the host molts. Repeated amputation of the regenerate shows that the adult leg is able to regenerate several times. We have a case in which the adult leg regenerated three times under the influence of the young host. The molt that exposed the third regenerate was the last molt of the host. These experiments show very clearly that the adult leg tissue has not lost its regeneration potential.

WIGGLESWORTH: How much of the base of the leg do you have?

BODENSTEIN: Part of the coxa and some body wall.

WIGGLESWORTH: Have you determined how much you have to have?

BODENSTEIN: Yes; to prevent regeneration, quite a bit of material needs to be extirpated. The more you take away, the longer it takes to regenerate a harmonious leg. As many as four molts may be needed.

WIGGLESWORTH: Then the really key part is beyond the coxa.

SCHNEIDERMAN: Are there any other comments on regeneration in general?

SCHARRER: Supernumerary molts as they were described in this type of experiment need not necessarily equal supernumerary molts occurring, for example, after implanting corpora allata in last instars. Because, if that were so, then all insect species would have to have the same number of molts, whereas actually closely related species may have twelve molts or six, respectively, and you do have variations even within one species. What you need for a normal molt is the proper hormone balance, so that these supernumerary molts may well be molts of a kind which are obtained under normal conditions in animals with a higher molting rate. In other cases where supernumerary molts are due to an experimentally changed endocrine situation and you do get intermediate forms, your argument is, in my opinion, not necessarily valid.

O'FARRELL: I would entirely agree with you that there is a very big sort of difference between this supernumerary molt and the one which

149

one gets in parabiosis or implantation, but it is difficult to understand what is going on in relation to timing of molting in a simple single regeneration process unless you tie it up in some way with the over-all molting cycle and humoral control. It is not easy to see, if one takes the results *in toto,* alternative explanations for the delays in molting. That being so, one assumes that the supernumerary molts are also due to interference in hormone balance. I know that it would be no more than an assumption at this stage.

WOLSKY: I should like to make a remark on the cytological basis of regeneration when regenerating appendages have fewer segments than the normals but these are larger than the originals. This is quite a general phenomenon in Hemiptera, in which the antenna on one side or the other breaks off in a nymphal stage and a regenerate appears in its place with a reduced number of segments. The segments of these incomplete regenerates are usually larger than normal, as if the loss of a segment were compensated for by excessive growth. Normally, the antennae have four segments but only three after regeneration, but they are larger. This was often observed in Hemiptera in nature and was generally considered as a case of compensatory hypertrophy. But nothing was known about its immediate causes. Recently in our laboratory, cytologists working on nymphal stages of Hemiptera (*Lygaeus, Oncopeltus*) find that their cells have a curious systematic increase in chromosome numbers from instar to instar, due to endomitotic nuclear divisions, as described by Geitler. This happens in most nuclei in quite different tissues. Now we think that here we may have a cytological explanation of this compensatory hypertrophy. The new regenerated segments will be bigger simply because the cells are bigger which form them. I made a few observations which are very preliminary and are highly disappointing from the point of view of demonstrating hyperregeneration, because these insects seem to be poor regenerators. I have only a few cases, and in these the regenerates are smaller than the normals. A closer look, however, shows that the diameters of the regenerates are very much bigger. I think that this could be of some importance in the problem of regeneration.

O'FARRELL: I should have mentioned that, although the number of segments in the normal leg remains constant, the number of segments in the cercus of *Blattella* increases by one at each molt—four, five, six, seven, even up to ten or eleven in the adult. The regenerated cercus is always at least one segment short, as compared with the normal cercus on the other side. This is something for which I can see no rational explanation at all.

BLISS: With reference to the supernumerary molts, it would appear that they are induced by the repeated removal of a limb following its regeneration.

O'FARRELL: That is so. They never occur in control animals.

BLISS: There is an interesting point about crustacean regeneration. If only one or two limbs are autotomized and if environmental conditions are unfavorable for a molt, *G. lateralis* will not undergo premolt limb regeneration, nor will it molt. It will do so only if environmental conditions are favorable. In other words, the removal of one or two limbs does not induce a molt. But if the number of limbs removed reaches five or more, the animal regenerates and molts despite unfavorable environmental conditions. This suggests that if enough limbs are lost, the loss per se can induce molting.

### ROLE OF HORMONES AND NERVES IN REGENERATION

SCHNEIDERMAN: Dr. Bodenstein will consider the role of nerves in regeneration. After this Dr. Sang will discuss nutritional questions, which we have so far avoided but which are important. And the final time can be devoted to the terminal question of the third day's discussion, namely, the special contribution of entomology to the study of morphogenesis.

BODENSTEIN: My comments, as will soon become evident, will perhaps more confuse than enlighten you concerning the role of hormones in regeneration and development. All the experiments reported here were performed on the American cockroach, *Periplaneta americana*. The nymphal forms of these insects regenerate their legs well, while the adults do not regenerate their legs. Yet one can induce leg regeneration in the adult by transplanting prothoracic glands. The adult leg can also be made to regenerate by transplanting it into a nymphal host. Here the prothoracic gland hormone of the nymph causes the adult tissues to express the regenerative capacities. The transplantation of the prothoracic gland into adult animals not only causes regeneration but also induces a molt in the adult. I have not seen any adult animal that was induced to molt in which I did not also observe regeneration in an amputated leg. Regeneration and molting must indeed be closely related. Sometimes, after prothoracic gland transplantation, one finds in the adult leg the beginnings of regenerative events which continue for a certain period of time and then cease to progress further. Such animals never molt. The transplantation of additional glands into such individuals always causes the continuation of regeneration and finally leads to molting. The appearance of the regenerate can be considered as the first visible sign of prothoracic gland hormone activity, for the regenerate seems to respond to a lower titer of prothoracic gland hormone than that needed for molting. But, in order to assure a continuation of the regenerative processes at least up to a definite stage of development, a certain hormone titer has to be maintained. There seems to be no doubt that the prothoracic gland hormone is necessary for the initiation and, to some extent, for the continuation of leg regeneration. One should therefore expect the extirpation of the prothoracic gland in nymphal stages to prevent the regeneration of the nymphal leg. When this experiment is performed, one finds that the nymphal legs do not lose their power of regeneration. Amputated nymphal legs in nymphs from which the prothoracic gland has been removed regenerate not only once but several times. Such animals also molt. Some years ago Pflugfelder showed in the walking stick that the corpora allata were responsible for regeneration. These animals lost their regenerative capacities after allatectomy but regained the power of regeneration after reimplantation of these glands. In recognition of these facts, we allatectomized nymphal roaches and found no effect on their ability to regenerate legs. In order to clarify this issue further, we extirpated in the nymphal stage the various glands of internal secretion, either separately or in combination, but again could find no effect on regeneration. Since regeneration and molting in adult animals can also be brought about by connecting nymphs with adults in parabiosis, we continued our extirpation experiments on such pairs. The most drastic operation was performed as follows: The prothoracic gland was removed from a last-stage nymph, and the animal was then allowed to metamorphose. This adult animal was combined with a younger nymph in parabiosis. Then the corpora allata and cardiaca were removed from both partners and so was the brain, subesophageal ganglion, and the prothoracic gland of the nymphal partner. Thus only the neurosecretory tissues of the adult brain were left intact in this pair. In spite of the removal of all these glands, the young partner induced molting and regeneration in the legs of both partners.

The entire problem becomes even more puzzling, as shown by the following results. In connection with studies on nerve regeneration in adult animals, all the nerves between the metathoracic ganglion and the metathoracic leg were cut, and the leg was then amputated by autotomy. The muscle potentials of the denervated coxal muscles were then tested by placing two small stimulating and recording electrodes in the coxa. This procedure was repeated about five to six times during a 2-month interval on thirty adult animals. To repeat, only the muscle potential measurements were performed as indicated; the entire endocrine system was left untouched. Of these thirty animals, three regenerated and molted. The reason is obscure. Because these experiments involved the severing of the nerves and the piercing of the coxal skin to insert the electrodes, three new sets of experiments were designed in which these procedures were performed separately. In one series, only the nerves were cut; in another one, only small needle punctures were made; and in the third, the nerves were cut and the coxal skin punctured. Each series consisted of twenty adult animals in which one leg of each individual was amputated by autotomy. The animals were observed for 6 months, during which no sign of regeneration was found. Now the only difference between the original experiment and the latter three experiments was that the animals in the original series received small electric shocks. These shocks, it was thought, might have stimulated the neurosecretory cells of the brain to renewed activity. The adult animals in this series possessed no prothoracic gland, which is a target for the brain hormone. On the possibility that the electric shock stimulated the brain and that the brain hormone could be held responsible for the observed regeneration of the legs in the original experiment, the transplantation of active nymphal brains should yield the same result. Now I should say that it is difficult in our material to select active brains, for we cannot stage the animals so well. We just took brains from individuals far advanced in their intermolt period and transplanted three brains into one host, in the hope that at least one of these brains was an active one. Of twenty such animals, perfect leg regeneration was induced in three. When these individuals were dissected, it was found that the prothoracic gland had regenerated also. Clusters of glandular tissues had appeared along the muscle core of the gland. These sites of regeneration varied in size; some consisted of smaller, others of larger, cell masses.

From these experiments one fact emerges clearly. The prothoracic gland is potentially able to regenerate its glandular cells. Whether the functional activity of the newly regenerated glandular parts is actually responsible for the observed induction of leg regeneration is by no means certain, since perfect regeneration was observed in one case in which the regenerated glandular structures were very inconspicuous. I tend to favor at present the view that under certain circumstances the brain hormone can take over the function of the prothoracic gland hormone. However, much more information is needed before we understand fully the action of this obviously very complicated system.

KARLSON: I hesitate to accept your conclusion that the prothoracic gland in this case is too small to produce enough hormone. A very small amount of tissue can react to the stimulus of an active brain; and if we assume a feedback control mechanism as in the pituitary-adrenal system of vertebrates, you would get more and more stimulation of the residual prothoracic gland cells by lack of prothoracic gland hormone. By this overproduction, the level necessary for molting can be reached. I wonder whether this could explain the baffling results of Chadwick, of cockroaches molting without prothoracic glands. In the normal course of events you have a feedback between prothoracic gland and brain. Here we can explain that the feedback is too small to affect the brain, and the brain becomes active, and the prothoracic gland will now overproduce. You have a higher hormone titer of a small number of cells.

BODENSTEIN: I agree with you on one point, for I believe, as you do, that there is a feedback mechanism from the prothoracic gland to the brain. But in our experiments the prothoracic gland was taken out, and in the absence of this structure there is, of course, no backfire possible. This also applies to Chadwick's experiments, where molting occurred after the extirpation of the prothoracic gland.

KARLSON: I understand that there is some regeneration of the prothoracic gland in these animals.

BODENSTEIN: The described prothoracic gland regeneration occurs only in experiments in which adult animals were used. Here the remnants of the metamorphosed prothoracic gland were present, and only here could we observe prothoracic gland regeneration.

SCHNEIDERMAN: Do you have an explanation of Chadwick's results?

BODENSTEIN: I only speculated about the possibility that, in Chadwick's extirpations and also, of course, in mine, not all prothoracic gland material was removed. This gland may have another as yet unknown branch which we have missed. I must add, however, that, so far, any attempt to discover this hypothetical branch in *Periplaneta* has met with failure, although quite a bit of effort was spent in search of it. At present—and I repeat—I feel that the possibility that the brain hormone takes over the function of the prothoracic gland hormone must still be seriously considered.

SCHNEIDERMAN: An alternative explanation would be that the prothoracic gland, when it is there, is the primary preferential site of the brain hormone action, but blood cells or some other tissue are also receptors. This seems unlikely, and I still find it hard to believe that you can get molting without prothoracic glands.

SCHARRER: Are there not cases in which the prothoracic gland can be bypassed in the control of molting?

SCHNEIDERMAN: I did not know that there was any evidence. There is some slight evidence that the brain can be bypassed. The isolated abdomen of *Cecropia* will never develop under its own power because it does not have the necessary endocrine systems.

BODENSTEIN: Since we know that the prothoracic gland can regenerate, any portion of this gland left in the animal after extirpation has, of course, the potentiality to regenerate. In adult animals in which the prothoracic gland is broken down, reserve cells from which the regenerates take their origin must be maintained, for otherwise we cannot understand the re-formation of glandular tissues. Whether these reserve cells, by themselves, continue to be active and thus even in the adult guarantee the maintenance of a low hormone titer is, of course, not known.

WIGGLESWORTH: I have no explanation of this, but the local effects of injury in the epidermis are so similar to the effects of the prothoracic gland hormone as to have led to the suggestion that local effects of wound healing are certainly due to the production of some diffusible substance which causes local growth. The effects are so similar as to have led to the suggestion that that substance may be ecdysone or something rather similar to it. Is it possible that your cockroaches, which are somewhat primitive insects, retain that property in the general epidermis as well as in these specialized ectodermal cells which form the prothoracic gland?

BODENSTEIN: In answer to your question whether the nerves are necessary for regeneration, I must admit that I do not know. There is a good reason for this lack of knowledge. Let me explain. The nerves of insects are supposed not to regenerate. Therefore, it should be a simple matter to denervate the leg, amputate it, and then see what happens. This experiment was performed on *Periplaneta*. Such legs regenerate almost as well as normal legs; there is only a slight delay of perhaps 5 days in the onset of regeneration. The denervated legs also contain their normal muscle complement. Thus it seems that regeneration takes place in the absence of nerves. But this is not true, for on closer examination one finds that the nerves also have regenerated and grown into the regenerate. As a matter of fact, it has been impossible so far to devise an experiment in which one could be absolutely sure that no nerves have grown into the regenerate. By extirpating the entire metathoracic ganglion, we hoped to prevent the nerves from growing into the leg. But it was found that a large number of nerve fibers grew out from the cut commissures, some of which almost certainly reached the leg.

I might also mention that the process of reinnervation of the denervated muscles has been checked electrically. Denervated coxal muscles become electrically unexcitable about 5 days after nerve severing. This period of inexcitability lasts for about a month, after which the muscles regain their excitability. When this occurs, the regenerating nerve fibers have apparently reached and re-established their muscle connection. Histological observations have confirmed this. Now as far as the regeneration of the denervated leg stump is concerned, I mentioned before that the onset of regeneration is delayed for about 5 days. Since the re-innervation of the denervated muscle occurs, according to the electrical and histological evidence, at a much later time, it appears as if regeneration takes place in the absence of nerves, but one cannot be too sure about this point, for a small number of nerve fibers might have reached the denervated region much sooner. This small number may be enough to assure regeneration. The question of the importance of the nerves for regeneration is still much unsettled in insects in spite of some previous work done on this problem.

SCHNEIDERMAN: I think of the experiments of Hans Nüsch of Basel in particular, in which he removed various segmental ganglia from pupal *Polyphemus* and showed that a normal leg would develop but the imaginal myoblasts would not, so that the leg had no muscles. This is certainly a case where development is under the influence of nerves.

BODENSTEIN: Yes, there seems to be no doubt that nerves are necessary for the differentiation of the imaginal muscles in the pupa. But this might be different in regeneration. One point, however, is clear in our experiments. If the newly formed muscles in the regenerate need nerves for their differentiation, there is no nerve-muscle specificity involved, for in the ganglion extirpation experiments the nerves come from a different ganglion.

SCHNEIDERMAN: Do you have ideas of the kind of experiments you could do to decide the question of nerve regeneration in insects?

BODENSTEIN: Yes, I think one has to do a great deal of histological work really carefully, the hard way.

BLISS: Does Dr. Bodenstein know of the work of Needham on crustacean regeneration? Needham has reported that if he denervates a limb of *Asellus aquaticus* and then causes the limb to be autotomized, regeneration of the limb is markedly retarded.

BODENSTEIN: Yes, I know this work, but I believe that it is not convincing as far as this point is concerned. In settling this problem, one has to be certain that no nerve fibers are present, for it is possible that only a few fibers are needed. We know that, in vertebrates, nerves are necessary for regeneration but that a full nerve complement is not needed.

BLISS: Apparently, he believes that regeneration is completely inhibited until reinnervation occurs.

BODENSTEIN: I mentioned that the onset of regeneration in the denervated organ is delayed. It is just the time relation that is upset. Since nerve regeneration seems to take place very fast, one is not certain whether regeneration can occur without nerves.

SCHNEIDERMAN: If it is not true (and I am not ready to admit this) that the nerves are not necessary for regeneration in insects, then this is the case at least in vertebrates, since it has been established beyond doubt by Marcus Singer and others that regeneration will not occur in those vertebrates which do regenerate limbs unless nerves are present.

BODENSTEIN: Even that is not quite true. I have just come from a conference where on the first day we heard how important the nerves were, and the meeting ended with a paper showing that the nerves were not important at all! So the whole problem even in vertebrates is not quite settled.

O'FARRELL: Dr. Bodenstein, did you do any experiments in which you did not section the nerve until after the regeneration process was already under way?

BODENSTEIN: Yes; it has no effect. After a regenerate has reached a certain stage, nerve cutting has no effect even on the velocity of regeneration.

SCHNEIDERMAN: In regeneration of the muscles in the pupal thorax of *Polyphemus,* Hans Nüsch obtained a variable amount of muscle development, depending upon how many days after the initiation of development he extirpated the ganglion. It is clearly a quantitative thing.

BODENSTEIN: It is certainly true that in many cases nerves are important for the formation of muscles.

RIZKI: Is it possible to take the cut ends of nerves and put them in various kinds of capillaries and then see what time is required for the regeneration of muscles?

BODENSTEIN: It is possible, but the time factor will not mean much because the operation is too drastic in such experiments. Those experiments are important for studies of nerve direction but are not well suited for studies of timing.

NUTRITIONAL EFFECTS ON DEVELOPMENT

SANG: The well-known nutritionally induced morphogenetic differences found among the Hymenoptera, and particularly Salt's classic case of male dimorphism in *Trichogramma semblidis,* where the alternative forms are elicited by differences in the nourishment consumed during development, have long suggested that some of the topics which we have discussed could be examined by nutritional techniques. This has now become a practical possibility, since a number of insects have been grown aseptically on chemically defined media, the diets being surprisingly similar for the few species yet studied. In the case of *Drosophila,* for which most is known, minimal requirements have also been determined quantitatively, so that the precise regulation of the supply of this or that nutrient is possible, offering the prospect of modifying the growth, development, and metamorphosis of the species in specific, desired directions; but examples are still few and inadequate, since little work of this kind has been attempted. Our great knowledge of *Drosophila* genetics should help in the elucidation of the effects of nutritionally induced developmental changes, but there are so many gaps in our information concerning the physiology of the developing fly that the nutritional approach, with all its inherent limitations, will first have to be explored empirically. Even so, certain lines of work can already be suggested.

Specific nutritional deficiencies, in an otherwise balanced diet, inevitably slow growth. What is important in the present context is that they do so in a regular fashion, so regular, indeed, that *Drosophila* can be used for the assay of particular nutrients, as the response to thiamine exemplified. However, not every strain behaves in precisely the same way, and some strains may display significant differences in minimal requirements because of genetic differences between them. Generally speaking, when the dietary deficiency is not great, development is merely prolonged, and size and survival are almost normal. Greater deficiencies prolong development further and cause a reduction in size and an increase in pupal mortality. Still greater deficiencies usually cause a high larval mortality, and the size of survivors is then very small. Flies weighing as little as 0.3 mg., compared with 1.2 mg. for a normal female, may emerge from the late-formed pupae, and one can only be impressed with the homeostatic mechanism which allows development to proceed to completion under such adverse conditions. We have largely ignored the character and importance of these mechanisms in our discussions, but they may impose an important limitation on the experimental manipulation of insect material; certainly they are worth examining in themselves.

No detailed studies have been made to see whether deprivation of particular vitamins produces specific syndromes of the kinds which they cause in mammals; they are usually recorded only as resulting in early larval death and in complete non-specific inhibition of development.

But careful studies may show specific changes, since, for example, Sanker and Sarma find that biotin deficiency results in degeneration of the fat body and of the gut of the rice moth (*Corcyra cephalonica*) and Sang that folic acid deficiency prevents full development of the adult ovary and the eclosion of *Drosophila* pupae. Again we have another aspect of the subject worth closer scrutiny.

One instance in which particular effects of nutritional deficiencies have been examined is given, since it also involves another aspect of growth which we have ignored, namely, the relation of cell size and cell number to total size. While selecting for size in *Drosophila*, F. W. Robertson noted that increased size in the strain used was due mainly to an increase in cell number and that variability at a particular level of selection was primarily due to cell size. That is, selection and environmental effects appeared to be acting on these two separate aspects of size, and it was of some interest to find whether they could be separated from each other by nutritional means. This was examined by reducing size by graded dietary deficiencies, and it was found that casein deficiencies had their main effect on cell number and choline deficiencies their main effect on cell size, showing clearly that the two components of size could be separately modified. Further work demonstrates that this result is not necessarily a general one; other strains respond differently, and other dietary deficiencies may also have specific consequences. The general situation is complex and has not yet been worked out, but it illustrates my point concerning the need for detailed studies of nutritional effects. In this case examination of size, as such, is no guide to what is happening, since flies of the same size may have different numbers or sizes of cells. It may also be worth emphasizing that this example raises the question of where the homeostatic mechanisms come into size determination and of how they produce their end results; a given size may be attained in two or more ways.

Not all development is precisely regulated, otherwise the many genetic abnormalities with which we are familiar would not be found: certain developmental abnormalities fall out with the control of the homeostatic mechanisms. One such gene mutation, which causes flies to develop without antennae, can have its phenotypic effect negated by nutritional means. An additional supply of riboflavin in the diet makes genotypically Antennaless larvae develop into flies with normal antennae. Another example, in which tryptophane has been found to play a significant role in altering the expression of Erupt eyes and the prevalence of tumors in *Drosophila*, has been studied by Plaine and Glass. Indeed, many mutants exist which show so-called "emergence effects" (e.g., eyeless, abnormal abdomen, etc.), and some may have their phenotypic effects modified by nutritional manipulation. Such mutants may be of value in indicating what biochemical mechanisms are abnormal and, as Plaine and Glass have noted, may provide material for analysis of biochemical systems like those made familiar from work with *Neurospora*.

Conversely, copies of mutants can be produced by feeding analogs and similar abnormal nutrients to developing *Drosophila* larvae, as Schultz *et al.* have shown. These phenocopies again suggest an approach to the mechanisms which control particular developmental patterns. Unfortunately, most of the work on phenocopies has involved non-specific agents, such as radiations of various sorts; but, even so, it is clear that a specific change is produced only when the agent is applied during a particular stage of development, and this is also true for the few specific agents tested. These agents have a restricted time of action, outside which they produce no morphoses. Consequently, it seems likely that analogs fed at particular times should produce more striking effects than those found by Schultz *et al.* and give more direct information about the mechanisms underlying particular developmental systems. In fact, this technique may be as useful as tissue culture methods for studying the development of particular organs.

Finally, it is necessary to mention adult nutrition, since this may affect the composition of the egg, and there is evidence that both mortality prior to hatching and subsequent rate of larval development can be modified by the quality of the food supplied to the mother, as Robertson and Sang have shown. Indeed, the nutrition of the female when she was a larva may influence the rate and success of development of her progeny. This carry-over from one generation to the next may provide a possible explanation of the problem raised earlier by Lees. However that may be, it is obvious that a study of maternal nutrition is necessary if any attempt is to be made to modify embryonic development; and this subject has scarcely been examined at all.

Some of these suggestions for modifying growth and development by nutritional means may prove to be overoptimistic; certainly, their applications will be limited to particular kinds of problems. But Hadorn's great success in applying chromatographic methods to problems of developmental genetics encourages one to think otherwise, since they have shown, among other things, differences which might also have been found by nutritional studies. So also does Schultz, Rothman, and Aranson's finding that related compounds of biological interest generally show similar morphogenetic effects. The thesis put forward here is, then, that one application of our newer knowledge of insect nutrition lies in deliberately altering the food, particularly the larval food, so as to create an internal environment which will modify the development of the embryonic cells which will later form the adult organism—in effect, use the larva as the tissue culture medium for these cells and take advantage of known genetic abnormalities for such work.

KARLSON: The carry-over effect is also known in *Ephestia,* strain A. If larvae are injected with abundant kynurenine, the female moths develop dark eyes, and the eggs they lay contain enough kynurenine for pigmentation of the gonads of the larvae; but in late larvae it is used up, and the moths developing then have the red eyes characteristic of strain A. It is quite the same thing.

HADORN: In connection with the report of Dr. Sang, I should like to discuss the results we got by using chromatographic and electrophoretic methods in studying the mutants Letal-translucida (*ltr*) and Letal-meander (*lme*) of *D. melanogaster*. The main results and their interpretation will be published in the 1956 volume of the Cold Spring Harbor Symposia. Both mutants interfere with the protein metabolism; but there are characteristic and locus-specific differences.

The *lme,* which dies during the third larval instar, is unable to digest food proteins in the second half of larval life. We find, therefore, a marked deficiency in all essential amino acids which no longer appear in the hemolymph. It has been clearly shown that homogenates of *lme*-intestine have lost almost all protease activity. Thus the *lme*-locus must be engaged in the formation of proteolytic enzymes. The *ltr,* which dies during pupal life, accumulates tremendous amounts of free amino acids in the hemolymph. These building blocks cannot be used, however, for protein synthesis. We therefore find a deficiency in proteins. Since the total nitrogen and the dry weight show normal values, we see that this genotype grows during the period which leads to lethal crisis only on the low level of amino acids and peptides, whereas normal genotypes build up their body proteins. Thus the *ltr*-locus has an important function with respect to protein synthesis. We need many more investigations of this kind before we shall be able to understand the gene-conditioned processes which control growth and metamorphosis in insects.

WADDINGTON: Have you any views as to how close to the gene this action on the proteins is? If you have a morphological mutant, presumably it would build up quite different proteins, use up quite different amino acids, and its hemolymph would be different from a normal one. One does not know whether the prime action of the gene is on protein synthesis or how far the effects on proteins or amino acids which you detect should be regarded as secondary consequences of a gene which is operating in some way. We have really no idea where the primary action of the gene is.

HADORN: So far I do not see any possibility of attacking this question.

KARLSON: I would propose to investigate the amount of ribonucleic acid present in these flies unable to synthesize proteins. If we assume that RNA is necessary for protein synthesis, they contain perhaps less RNA; this would, biochemically, account for the deficiency.

THE SPECIAL CONTRIBUTIONS OF ENTOMOLOGY TO MORPHOGENESIS

SCHNEIDERMAN: Shall we now turn to the final question, of the special contributions of entomology to morphogenesis? This is not a topic which can be easily covered in half an hour, and it has not been done justice because of time limitations. Dr. Wigglesworth has some comments.

WIGGLESWORTH: We might consider whether this final exercise is worth while. I understand that the proceedings of this symposial chat are to be published. If they are published and if they should by chance ever be read, one would hope that they might possibly attract readers outside this field, and, if that should happen, it may be useful to have some points made under this final heading, because we can say (within these four walls) that many students of growth are woefully ignorant of just these points. We all feel here that entomology has some very special contributions to make to the field of morphogenesis. Insects are small creatures, and their visible parts are formed by a single layer of epidermal cells which lay down a cuticle responsible for their visible morphology. There is a good deal of evidence to support the view that the form of the insect is very largely determined by the growth activities of that single layer of epidermal cells. That fact makes the study of insects wonderful material for the study of morphogenesis. I propose to consider only two points, because I think this should be a free-for-all. It does not matter that in our opinion the points to be made should all be very obvious ones. The ones I propose to make are very obvious. The first one arises from Dr. O'Farrell's communication this afternoon. I think that that was one of the most interesting communications we have had, in the extent to which it provokes thought. You are causing this peripheral injury, removing a leg, and a message is sent to the animal, "Hold up growth for a few days, and we shall be able to make a new leg." The first point I am making is the wonderful opportunity that insects provide for the study of the integration of the organism. The second point is this: I think it is fantastic, really, that we should have gathered here to discuss the physiology of insect growth and development and have no discussion upon the action of the corpus allatum hormone, which I have got into the way of calling the "juvenile hormone" or, when pressed by certain people to give it a Greek name, I called it "Neotenin." That is not a new name; it is the same as "juvenile," but Greek instead of Latin. If I may say this without prejudice, I think that this is one of the most interesting hormones known to endocrinology, and it has been known to endocrinology for twenty years. When I say known to endocrinology, I do not mean known to endocrinologists! If you study that excellent book, *Analysis of Development*, edited by Willier, Weiss, and Hamburger, you will find the section on metamorphosis simply does not reflect the state of knowledge or, in my opinion, the very great importance of this system for an understanding of growth.

Concerning the last question to which we are invited to give an answer—"Can the return of differentiated tissues to an earlier hormonal milieu actually revert them to a precursor state?"—that is just one of the many problems which come up for discussion in connection with the corpus allatum hormone. The real point is that you have a growth system made up of a single layer of epidermal cells which can be deflected into the most fantastically different courses of morphogenesis (when you think, for example, of the caterpillar, its pupa, and the final moth) simply by differences in concentration and timing in the secretion of what is almost certainly a comparatively simple chemical substance. That is surely a hormone of the very greatest interest. And now that Williams has obtained active extracts of this hormone, we shall hope to have it concentrated and purified, and I hope before long a really wide interest will be taken in it. That, Mr. Chairman, is my sole contribution—a very obvious one.

SCHNEIDERMAN: I am sure there are other comments. The only one I would make is that this juvenile hormone will surely be of interest to people who study caste determination in termites and bees, phase transformations in grasshoppers, and myriads of other problems. In addition, it is, as was pointed out, a very potent insecticide, because, when applied topically, it has the effect of preserving the larval characters in that local place.

WADDINGTON: From the point of view of one whose interest is in experimental embryology in a number of other groups and who has worked largely with vertebrates, I think the thing that strikes the vertebrate worker as being particularly interesting in insects is, first of all, that you have this periodic phenomenon of a succession of instars, that you keep on going through a cycle in a way that vertebrates do not, with this extraordinarily interesting and complex balance of hormones controlling the whole thing. And then it is also an extraordinary aspect of insects that their development can go so far as to provide you with totally different developmental systems, all based on the same set of genes. You have the egg of *Drosophila* developing into a larva, and the imaginal buds inside the larva then developing into something completely different from a morphological point of view. I cannot think that any other group but insects really provides you with that type of material. There is one further rather special point about insects, I think. They seem to provide a great many more examples than most groups of differentiation going on in only single cells or in groups of two or four cells, often depending upon a process of differential cell division. I am sorry that we have not had more of the Henke group, who are working on that aspect. The final point is that insects happen to offer much more favorable material than anything else for studying the mechanism of gene action in organisms. Admittedly, other groups probably could do this, but we happen to know more at the moment about insects.

HADORN: I should like to say one thing about sex differentiation. Again it is possible to see what a single cell is doing. I referred in Providence to the work of Seiler in Zurich on the moth *Solenobia*. If he gets, for instance, an intersexual antenna, he has shown very clearly that it is a mosaic of female and male cells, each cell doing its own job, and thus what looks like an intermediate organ is a mosaic of pure male and pure female cells. Seiler had to go down to the electron microscope to show that each cell can be classified as either male or female. Thus in insects we have the most beautiful system of alternative reaction norms.

LEES: I should like to put in a word for insects as material for studying control of development by the external environment. Although the effects of day length were first discovered in plants, comparable phenomena were soon revealed in insects and vertebrates. Despite a long period of neglect, the large volume of recent research on insect photoperiodism has shown, I think, how favorable this material really is. One very simple reason for this is the comparatively rapid development of insects. Experiments on photoperiodism are extremely time-consuming. Yet many lines of attack which are virtually impossible with vertebrate material are open to the insect physiologist.

164

# *Postscript*

The conference closed with expressions of thanks by the chairman, Dr. Max Day, to all concerned. As he did not comment on the conference at that time, a few words in retrospect may be desirable here.

The general chairman had hoped that all discussion could be centered on issues and that factual material would be presented only to the extent that it bore on those issues. However, the conference fell short of this ideal procedure, for discussion was usually incited by a specialist speaking at some length on his own research. To that extent the conference followed the pattern of a symposium. However, it was much more informal than the typical symposium, and discussion ranged freely, with little restraint as to time or subject. At the beginning of the second session on embryology the above-mentioned ideal was approached when vigorous discussions on certain aspects of morphogenesis were set off merely by questions posed by the chairman.

At no time during the three days of the conference did interest flag; always someone had something to say or slides to show on the topic of the moment. Discussion was not dominated by a few persons; there were various combinations of speakers, suggesting that the desired interplay of different experiences and points of view was actually achieved. If degree of enthusiasm of participants at a conference is proportional to its subsequent beneficial effects, the present conference will produce a high yield.

F. L. C.

# Selected Bibliography

BLISS, DOROTHY E. Neurosecretion and the control of growth in a decapod crustacean. *In:* Bertil Hanstrom: zoölogical papers in honour of his sixty-fifth birthday, November 20, 1956, ed. K. G. WINGSTRAND, pp. 56–75. Lund, Sweden: Zoölogical Institute, 1956.

BODENSTEIN, D. Endocrine mechanisms in the life of insects. Recent Progr. Hormone Res., **10**:157–82, 1954.

———. Embryonic development. Postembryonic development. Regeneration. Role of hormones in molting and metamorphosis. *In:* Insect physiology, ed. K. D. ROEDER, chaps. 29–32. New York: John Wiley & Sons, 1953.

HADORN, E. Patterns of biochemical and developmental pleiotropy. Cold Spring Harbor Symp. Quant. Biol., **21**:363–73, 1956.

———. Genetik und Entwicklungsphysiologie. Naturwissenschaften, pp. 85–91, 1953.

KARLSON, P. Biochemical studies on insect hormones. Vitamins & Hormones, **14**:222–66, 1956.

KLEINHOLZ, L. H. Endocrinology of invertebrates, particularly of crustaceans. *In:* Recent advances in invertebrate physiology, ed. B. T. SCHEER, pp. 173–93. ("University of Oregon Publications.") Eugene, Ore., 1957.

KÜHN, ALFRED. Vorlesungen über Entwicklungsphysiologie. Berlin and Göttingen: Springer-Verlag, 1955.

LEES, A. D. The physiology of diapause in Arthropods. ("Cambridge monographs in experimental biology," Vol. **1**.) London: Cambridge University Press, 1955.

PFLUGFELDER, O. Entwicklungsphysiologie der Insekten. Leipzig: Akademische Verlagsgesellschaft, Geest & Portig K.-G., 1952.

POULSON, D. F. Chromosomal control of embryogenesis in *Drosophila*. Am. Naturalist, **79**:340–63, 1945.

SANG, J. H. The quantitative nutritional requirements of *Drosophila melanogaster*. J. Exper. Biol., **33**:45–72, 1956.

SCHARRER, B. Hormones in invertebrates. *In:* The hormones, ed. G. PINCUS and K. V. THIMANN, **3**:57–95. New York: Academic Press, 1955.

SCHARRER, B., and SZABO LOCHHEAD, M. Tumors in the invertebrates: a review. Cancer Res., **10**:403–19, 1950.

SCHARRER, E., and SCHARRER, B. Hormones produced by neurosecretory cells. Recent Progr. Hormone Res., **10**:183–240, 1954.

WADDINGTON, C. H. Principles of embryology. New York: Macmillan Co., 1956.

———. The strategy of the genes. New York: Macmillan Co., 1957.

WAGNER, R. P., and MITCHELL, H. K. Genetics and metabolism. New York: John Wiley & Sons, 1955.

WEISS, P. Principles of development. New York: Henry Holt & Co., 1939.

WIGGLESWORTH, V. B. The physiology of insect metamorphosis. ("Cambridge monographs in experimental biology," Vol. 1.) London: Cambridge University Press, 1954.

———. The principles of insect physiology. Rev. ed. London: Methuen & Co., 1950.

WILLIER, B. A., WEISS, P., and HAMBURGER, V. Analysis of development. Philadelphia: W. B. Saunders Co., 1955.

WYATT, S. SILVER. Culture in vitro of tissue from the silkworm, *Bombyx mori* L. J. Gen. Physiol., **39**:841–52, 1956.

PRINTED IN U.S.A.